Surviving ME

Surviving ME

Practical Strategies for
Coming to Terms with Chronic Fatigue

Joyce Fox

VERMILION
LONDON

First published in the United Kingdom in 1996 by Vermilion
an imprint of Ebury Press
Random House UK Ltd
Random House
20 Vauxhall Bridge Road
London SW1V 2SA

Random House Australia (Pty) Ltd
20 Alfred Street
Milsons Point Sydney
New South Wales 2016 Australia

Random House New Zealand Limited
18 Poland Road, Glanfield
Aukland 10 New Zealand

Random House South Africa (Pty) Limited
PO Box 337 Bergvlei South Africa

Random House UK Limited Reg. No. 954009

1 3 5 7 9 10 8 6 4 2

A CIP catalogue record for this book is available from
the British Library.

ISBN 0 09 181472 3

Typeset by Clive Dorman & Co
Printed by Mackays of Chatham, plc

Contents

Foreword

by *The ME Association*

Everybody who needs to know more about the reality of living with ME should read this book. Myalgic encephalomyelitis (ME) is a potentially severe, disabling and chronic disorder of the immune and central nervous systems that causes physical and cognitive problems. The symptoms are many and varied; they may differ from person to person and, because of their similarity to those of other illnesses, a diagnosis of ME may be overlooked by a GP or consultant, or not even recognised at all.

The cause is as yet unclear but in most cases it is linked to a viral infection. A cure is still elusive and treatments for various symptoms of the illness may help some people but not others. The outcome for individual cases is difficult to predict. Some will slowly return to normal or near normal health. Others will make variable progress but never achieve full recovery. A significant number remain chronically ill and severely disabled, making little or no progress, and a small number steadily deteriorate, becoming chair of bed-bound for much of the time.

It is estimated that up to 150,000 people in the UK alone are affected by ME. Many of these are children although for most people onset occurs between twenty and forty years of age. ME not only affects the lives of those with the illness, but family and friends as well. The cost of ME is incalculable; not least the human cost of shattered lives, lost careers, lost independence, and the damaging affect on relationships brought about by disbelief in an illness which is difficult to understand and is not fully accepted.

A number of books have been written about ME, both for medical professionals and for the general public, giving information about ME and good advice about managing the illness. However they tend to say little about the psychological and emotional impact of ME which can be as difficult to cope with as the physical symptoms. *Surviving ME* fulfils that need by providing people with ME, their families and carers, with advice on how to deal with the feelings and emotions that this invisible illness produces.

People with ME need help to adjust to the illness emotionally. To adjust to the loss of health, career and independence is to go through a form of bereavement, and an important part of the grieving process involves dealing with feelings of denial, anger and loss. Joyce Fox talks about feelings and emotions which are all too familiar to those with ME but are often not spoken about let alone addressed. She assures the reader that such feelings are quite normal and that once they have been acknowledged it is than easier to understand those feelings and learn how to cope with them. This book gently guides and supports the reader through this difficult process.

Problems encountered with relationships and health and welfare services are covered in a useful question and answer section, providing both information and much needed support.

I hope that if you have ME or someone you care for has ME, this valuable book will give you more understanding of the illness and, most importantly, a new appreciation of *living* with ME.

Mavis Moore
1 February 1996

Preface

This book is written from experience. Seven years ago I caught a bad case of 'flu which never quite went away. After a couple of months in bed my doctor diagnosed 'post-viral malaise' and advised me to return to work as soon as possible. Despite feeling unwell, I stumbled back to my job as a community worker if only on a very part-time basis. A year later, still not exactly sure what 'post-viral malaise' was and thinking that I would soon recover, I suffered a major relapse. This time I not only had to give up work but also going out altogether. I felt too ill to stand for more than a few minutes and over the following months found myself getting progressively worse. I was now virtually housebound and in bed for much of the day. I changed my doctor and received the diagnosis of ME.

Over the following year or so, encouraged by stories of recovery by this 'remedy' or that 'treatment', I went from one alternative therapy to another. By the time I had almost worked my way through the entire list of supposed cures I began to learn that the only real way of improving my chances of getting better was to listen to my body and rest as much as I needed. Learning to pace myself helped avoid further deterioration in my health and I managed to sustain, if not an improvement, at least the level of health that I still had.

Like so many people with ME the illness took its toll on my personal relationships. My family, even when they saw it with their own eyes, found my situation very difficult to accept. For a long time they could not believe that I was really this ill. They coped by explaining my ill health as merely the symptoms of stress and an over-sensitive character and interpreted my feelings of anger and despair as proof of this. Friends, uncomfortable with someone always ill in bed and no longer able to socialise, began to drop away.

At least my partner Frank, my link with the outside world, was still healthy and working. Then the unimaginable happened; one day Frank came home complaining that his usual walk to work was leaving him exhausted with aching legs. Soon he had to give up swimming and began reducing his time at work. A month later he was in bed with a 'flu-like illness which seemed to linger on and on. After more than six months of managing to do hardly more than just walk around the flat he too was diagnosed as having ME. We couldn't believe it, it was difficult enough to convince people that I had ME – how improbable was it going to appear now that both of us had it? Frank soon gave up work along with most of the other things that go with an active life.

So there we were – and still are – both sufferers and carers. It has not been easy but by being highly organised we have managed to continue living independently. Like so many of you reading this, we live day to day, getting as much as possible out of what we can still do and grieving over what we cannot. We, like you, continue each day to face the challenge of surviving ME.

Introduction

When I first became ill with ME, I read all the books on the subject that I could lay my hands on. I read about the history of the disease, about its various symptoms and about the different alternative therapies available which might help in some small way. I found this information useful but what I really wanted to know, what I was actually searching for between the pages of medical advice was how to cope with living with a disease that had wreaked havoc in my life. How was I going to come to terms with no longer being able to work, with losing my friends, with having to spend great tracts of time doing nothing because I was too exhausted to keep myself occupied? Moreover, what was I to do with all these new and alien feelings raging inside me: the panic, the frustration, the anger and despair? How was I going to avoid going completely mad with so much time on my hands to think? All these and a flood of other questions were urgently needing to be answered. And I was not alone; the more I spoke with other people with ME and their carers, the more I found that they too were feeling the same kinds of emotions and were asking the same sorts of questions. There was neither person nor book to advise us and reassure us that the emotional turmoil we felt was normal and understandable – we needed guidance and support.

I hope that this book provides that guidance and support for those of you who find yourself in the same situation. Rather than taking the medical approach covered more than adequately in other books it focuses on how to cope with having ME. It opens up the Pandora's Box and takes a close look at all those difficult, painful emotions that we wish we never felt yet are still very much there. It shows that these emotions are a valid expression of a real crisis in our lives and that we need to recognise and accept this. If we try to dismiss or ignore them we risk burying these feelings deeper inside and allowing them to fester and grow. Instead, we need to start to acknowledge these demanding emotions, understand them and finally deal with them. Only by taking these feelings seriously can we lessen their grip on us.

I am not going to pretend that this is an easy book. It does not skim over unpleasant feelings such as jealousy, shame or self-hate and offer glib and superficial solutions. It does not offer empty inspirational platitudes that promise self-healing by merely 'letting go' or by 'not being negative'.

What it does offer is the belief that truly to come to an acceptance of our lives as they are now, with all the losses incurred by ill health, we must face what we are actually feeling honestly and bravely, however distasteful, difficult or traumatic this may be. When we begin to acknowledge all the emotional hurts that we may have experienced at the hands of other people because we are ill; when we admit the pain of a long-term situation in which we endure constant physical debility, isolation, loss of self-worth; then we are one step closer to accepting ourselves, to recognising our courage and strength and one step nearer to demanding the respect that we deserve.

Many of you reading this will know bereavement through the loss of a family member or friend. When you lose someone you love, you often find that in your grief you pass through different stages of emotions before you are able to come to an acceptance of the situation: denial, anger, bargaining and depression. You may not experience all these feelings in this particular order but you will have to journey through a certain amount of emotional terrain before you are able to integrate the loss into your life.

But death is not the only sort of loss which can cause us to grieve. Many people experience similar feelings when they lose their job or their marriage breaks down. Losing your health, however, is one of the most fundamental losses that you can experience. Without a healthy body you cannot wholly live, and the more severely ill you are the greater the loss. Not only may you lose your job and all the things that go with it – a sense of usefulness and purpose, self-esteem, social recognition, self-respect in earning your living – you may well lose your friends, partner and the ability to do even the most basic of tasks for yourself. How can you help but grieve over these losses?

With the death of a loved one you grieve for the past, for what was, for what will never be. But their death happened on a particular day with each day of grieving the occasion of their death gets further and further away. You will never forget that person or the awful event that took them away from you, but eventually their death will seem more and more distant and the pain of bereavement, if properly expressed, will slowly heal.

With a chronic illness like ME the situation is different. The event that began your process of grieving – becoming ill – does not stay in the past. Living with ME means waking up each morning with the 'event', the reason for the loss you feel. Because you are ill all the time there is no moving away from it, no diminishing of the feelings of profound loss with the passage of time. There is no getting away from ME, you may have to deal with the same issues three years down the line as you did in the first weeks of becoming ill. This is what makes the disease such a challenge to deal with.

The stages of denial, anger, depression and acceptance in the grieving process are just that; stages. In chronic illness, particularly severe cases of ME, these stages are ongoing processes. You may feel anger in the first few months of your illness and go on to feel depressed, followed by an increased feeling of acceptance. A few weeks later, in response to your health getting worse, or losing a friend, or for apparently no reason at all you may again feel angry and depressed. And within these catch-all labels we call denial or anger or depression there are myriad of other emotions that you may also be struggling with; emotions such as jealousy, frustration, shame, guilt, to name but a few. You may not feel all of them, you may even find it difficult to admit that you feel any of them, but it is only natural that you will experience some with varying force at different points of your illness.

Focusing on the emotions that sufferers can experience when living with ME does not in any way mean that the cause of the disease is psychological. There is now scientific evidence to show that ME is an organic disease but until there is a diagnostic test there will continue to be controversy surrounding it. Understandably, those of us with the disease are sensitive to any suggestions that what we are experiencing is 'all in the mind'. ME is a physical disease but like any life crisis it involves great change and loss resulting in emotional pain. Acknowledging this, even in a climate of disbelief, is vital for those of us with the illness, our carers and those who wish to educate themselves through listening to our experiences.

Section one

THE EMOTIONS

1

Denial – Part One

When a major crisis occurs in your life the very first reaction is often complete denial. Whether that crisis is a death in the family, the break-up of a marriage or the sudden onset of a serious disease, the situation feels unreal. You may try to make sense of it yet have an overwhelming feeling of disbelief; you cannot believe this is happening to you. Even when others are telling you that it is happening and trying to make you face up to reality, all you want to do is run away and hide. But slowly the facts start to sink in and you begin to get used to the idea that your life has changed. Gradually, you emerge from your dream-like state and begin to feel ready to deal with your new situation.

With the onset of ME the very first reaction is also one of denial, but a denial of a very different kind. Instead of being told that you have a serious illness and you, in shock, denying it, the opposite is likely to occur. You know that there is something very seriously wrong with your health but your doctor does not take you seriously. Your family and friends, far from urging you to face up to what is happening, may not believe that you are really ill either. The normal process of denial is completely inverted. You know yourself that you are ill yet you are confronted with a seamless wall of disbelief from others. How can you express the usual kind of denial about your situation when nobody seems to believe that there is anything much wrong with you in the first place? And how will you be able to learn to accept your situation if you cannot even embark on the very first stage of the normal grieving process?

This unusual experience of denial is often the most demanding – and the most potentially damaging – aspect of living with ME. It can make you doubt your own sanity; how can I really be ill if no-one else thinks that I am? It can stop you taking the necessary precautions against relapse and lead you into increasing disability. It can make you feel ashamed of being ill, for having an illness like ME, for not recovering. It can hinder you from receiving the kind of care and treatment that you may need. It can even prevent you from accepting an eventual diagnosis. It can leave you isolated and alienated from family and friends. It can make you feel as if you are going half-crazy; having to live a very reduced life yet being doubted and dismissed wherever you go. It can leave you feeling quite unable even to begin to come to terms with your illness.

Dealings with Doctors

For most people the experience of being ill lasts no more than a couple of weeks. You start to feel unwell, go to the doctor, get a prescription and in a short while you are back in the swing of things feeling quite normal. In most cases ME starts as a diagnosis of flu and the first two weeks of it may feel no different from any other experience of minor ill health. The problem begins when this 'normal' period of illness expires.

Still feeling terrible, you return to your doctor and some tests are taken. Nothing shows up. The verdict;

'You probably haven't quite recovered from the flu yet. Get a bit more rest'.

You are sent away and spend another fortnight in bed – and then another. As weeks turn into months you realise that you are not getting better. You feel it is about time that you get some answers from your GP. Back in the surgery you explain that, despite a tremendous amount of resting, you feel exactly the same as you did at the beginning of your illness.

'Can't understand it' says the doctor, 'there doesn't seem to be anything wrong with you.'

You repeat how ill you are feeling. How can there be nothing wrong?

'How are you finding work these days?'

You remind him that he has been issuing sick notes for the last few months as you have been too poorly to work.

'Yes' he continues, 'but would you say that you find work stressful, that perhaps you're not looking forward to going back?'

You are not sure that you have heard correctly. Maybe you have not been making yourself clear.

'I'm here, Doctor, precisely because I am concerned that I

am *not* able to get back to work, because I feel too ill to even cook a meal and wash myself never mind even think about being able to spend a full day working.'

'So, how's your sex life?'

'I beg your pardon?'

'Your sex life. Having difficulty in your personal relationships? Feeling a bit anxious about life in general?'

Now you are really confused.

'If I am anxious it is only because I have been ill for months and you are acting as if it's all in my mind!'

You suddenly realise that you are getting nowhere. Your previously even-tempered, understanding, GP is now looking decidedly harassed and impatient. You reluctantly leave with the advice to return to work as soon as possible and to try and get out a bit more and see a few friends. You stagger home and collapse into bed.

You still feel lousy but now have something extra to worry about. Your doctor seems to believe that your aching limbs, your overwhelming exhaustion, your fevers and headaches are due simply to emotional factors. What are you going to tell your family? Perhaps the doctor is right; perhaps somehow, without you knowing it, you *are* covering up a dislike of work with these symptoms. Even though you feel that you would do anything to get back to the way things were before you became ill maybe you do, for some bizarre and unconscious reason, want to be ill in bed. You know it makes no sense, you know you are desperate to be well again yet how can you not believe your doctor, a member of a respected profession whom you have never previously had any reason to doubt, if he says there is nothing physically wrong with you.

Of course, each person's experience with their doctor will differ but the scene just sketched happens far too often. Time and time again, people (who have eventually received a positive diagnosis of ME), have told stories of their GP telling them that their symptoms are due to feeling afraid of life, of wanting the 'safety' of the confines of illness or the result of being depressed, under too much stress or of having an over-anxious, perfectionist attitude to life. One housebound sufferer was told that he had just too high expectations of life and that what he interpreted as feeling ill was normal health for everyone else. Of course, everyone else just got on with their lives without making such a fuss. This sort of 'diagnosis' is extremely damaging to your sense of who you are and you can quickly start to lose confidence in yourself. Even though you know that you have these physical symptoms, you may start to question your ability to judge whether they really are a sign of a serious illness or just – as your doctor seems to believe – a manifestation of a neurotic, depressive personality.

Despite the risk of being dismissed again you will probably seek out other doctors who may be able to give you a diagnosis that makes sense to you. It is not unknown for sufferers to do the rounds of GPs and be dismissed over and over again; their self-belief and esteem diminishing with every exchange. But, hopefully, you will find a doctor who has heard about ME and will make a clinical diagnosis based on the symptoms you describe together with the exclusion of other diseases that present in a similar way. Yet even with a diagnosis of ME your problems may not be over. Your new GP may only have a rudimentary knowledge of the illness, enough only to give you a shaky diagnosis. The tables were turned for one sufferer when his doctor asked *him* if he thought he might have ME 'I was rather hoping that you could tell me' was the obvious reply! Often, GPs give a positive diagnosis and then proceed with treatment that reveals a belief that ME is a predominantly psychological disorder. As a former headteacher, recently diagnosed with ME, explained:

'When I first received a diagnosis I was tremendously relieved. Having been sent packing by several doctors, I'd almost given up hope that my condition would be recognised. It was only after a few months that it became clear that my doctor had a rather different understanding of ME than I, or the ME organisations with whom I had contact, did. Every time I told him about a new symptom he explained it away. The swelling in my back was due to tension, the pain in my head was because I needed my eyes tested, my intolerance to food was due to my not eating enough fibre. Some of his explanations may have been correct, but I began to feel that ME was a symptomless disease!'

So even with a diagnosis you can still be left with the feeling that, perhaps, you are not really suffering from what you think you are, that maybe you are attributing symptoms to ME that are not part of the disease at all.

Why Doctors deny

The initial denial and dismissal of a little understood illness is not only confined to ME. In the biography of the famous cellist, Jacqueline du Pré, a very similar story is told of the treatment she received before eventually being diagnosed with MS. Despite having performed in front of thousands of people from a very early age, the first symptoms of her illness – feeling exhausted and finding it difficult to position her hands on the cello – were interpreted by those around her as stage fright, hysteria and a reluctance to perform. Until her symptoms became much more pronounced and it was discovered that she had MS, du Pré's ill health was blamed on her character.

With ME the denial that there is a physical reason for your symptoms is more profound and prolonged because of the considerable medical controversy still surrounding the disease. Despite recent advances in research showing that ME does have an organic basis, the evidence to date has not been conclusive enough to develop a diagnostic test. Without such a test, the medical profession at large have remained sceptical that the symptoms described by sufferers are entirely due to physical or neurological abnormalities in the body. They may be informed enough to identify symptoms as those of ME, but many doctors still believe that those symptoms – and therefore the disease itself – are largely psychological in origin. Thankfully, an increasing number of doctors do believe that ME is a genuinely physical disease and treat their patients accordingly.

General Practitioners are just that: practitioners with knowledge of general and common illness. They do not specialise, they cannot know about every disease in existence. Therefore, when they confront a condition that is unfamiliar to them they are more than likely to relate it to what they already know. They have a lot of experience with patients suffering from depression and stress-related conditions. According to one GP, about twenty to thirty per cent of patients visiting his surgery complain of feeling, 'tired all the time' – fatigue syndromes of one kind or another are extremely common.

When your doctor is presented with ME about which he knows very little it is easy for him to assume that it must be yet another of these stress/depression-related fatigue conditions. Yet if he listened carefully he might notice that the symptoms you describe are completely different to these syndromes, not least in their severity. The problem for the ME sufferer is that their doctor may *not* be listening carefully. S/he may also be acquainted with the 'organic versus psychological' debate around the disease and, in the absence of a diagnostic test, feel safer believing that ME is indeed a psychiatric condition – at least until conclusively proved otherwise. To a doctor who is uninformed about the illness and who has a natural leaning to believe that it is a kind of depressive illness, the symptoms that you present are swiftly interpreted to prop up this belief.

The way you describe your symptoms may also precipitate misdiagnosis. It can be very difficult to tell someone who you fear is already disbelieving exactly how ME feels. You may use words that fail to give a completely clear picture of what your symptoms are like. Trying to describe physical sensations that are new to you is a bit like learning a vocabulary for a foreign language. You may not have the correct word to express precisely what you want to say so you search for something similar in the hope that it will adequately get your meaning across but that, in reality, means something quite different.

People with ME, therefore, may use the word 'tired' when they really mean 'complete exhaustion after minimal activity'. They may say they 'ache all over' when in fact the pain in their arms after merely doing the washing up may be excruciating. On hearing the word 'tired' your doctor may well think you mean that you are feeling just a little more fatigued as you go about your normal daily routine; your meaning of 'tired' is completely lost on him. Even if you try to explain that a few months ago you used to enjoy hiking regularly, and now you have to sleep off a short walk, a picture of what he thinks you can do is already set in his mind by the particular words you have used.

The fact that mood-swings and depression are sometimes a feature in ME can further cloud the issue. These symptoms may be an organic part of the illness, a reaction to living with it, or a combination of both. But to many doctors, their very existence are just further evidence of a disease with a psychological cause. Again, with this in mind your doctor may misinterpret what you are telling him. You may try to explain what a struggle it is to carry on now that you can no longer do the things you used to and he may *hear* you say something entirely different. Because your doctor may be pre-judging you as having a psychiatric problem, your words are filtered through this perception and he may hear you say that the *reason* you can no longer do what you used to do is because you find life a struggle i.e. you are apathetic and depressed. So many ME sufferers go to see their doctor with a description of how the illness is affecting their life and return home with a completely different interpretation presented to them.

Doctors enjoy a certain status in society. This is based partly on our high expectations of the knowledge we think they should have, and partly in our willingness to hand over our power and believe that they really do 'know best'. They are trained in a scientific culture that demands irrefutable proof as evidence of the existence of disease. They work in a medical environment in which incontrovertible test results reign supreme. There are few doctors who have the courage to admit, 'I don't know' when faced with a mysterious and apparently new disease like ME. Most feel more comfortable and secure in their traditional role of being the one that knows. If only they would appreciate the importance of sympathy and kindness, of listening in a non-judgemental and respectful manner. If they would appreciate that to be a good doctor they do not have to have all the answers but they do have to offer simple caring – such as reassurance and encouragement. Every patient knows the difference such support can make in coping with a long-term illness.

Unfortunately, too many people with ME have a GP who listens just long enough to label them with the only other condition that needs no diagnostic test and seems to fit the bill; depression or 'ME' as a label for a syndrome which is psychological in origin. Even if the symptoms do not quite fit, even if the patient has experienced clinical depression before and tells their doctor that this illness feels completely different, the diagnosis is made because it is the easiest option. The only other option is to stick one's neck out and diagnose the 'real ME', a disease about which little is yet known and one that is not fully accepted as organic because science has yet to substantiate the disease to its satisfaction.

Telling family and friends

With all this uncertainty surrounding your illness, meanwhile, you have to deal with your family. Understandably, they want to know what the doctor has said. What is wrong with you?

Why are you so exhausted all the time? Will you be ill for long? Is there a cure? You hesitantly report what happened at the surgery. You tell them how confused you feel about what you have been told. You try to explain your anger that you have not been taken seriously. You share your fear that your doctor has either failed to pick up on some very serious cause of your ill health or that you have indeed lost your ability to judge how you feel. You know that how you feel cannot be due to stress or depression yet perhaps the doctor is right; perhaps you are just suffering from this and nothing else.

You look to your family for support. You want them to say that they are on your side, that you are not going mad, that you really are physically ill, despite what the doctor may believe. But without a firm diagnosis they may not be able to give you that kind of support. They too may feel uncertain about the reason for your ill health. Surely if there was something really wrong with you the doctor would know about it? How do you know that you are not just a little depressed as the doctor has suggested?

Of course, you do not know for sure, and there is no reason why they should believe you rather than your doctor. All you know is how ill you feel and that the advice to return to work as soon as possible seems like the worst thing to do. You do not feel well enough to even make the journey. But your family encourage you to take the doctor's advice – you never know, it might just be the tonic you need, they say. The next week you drag yourself back to work. Before long you feel feverish and sick, you tell yourself that if you just take things steady you will be all right, but ten minutes later you are so ill that you have to be taken home by a colleague.

Several months on and you are still off work, and your family are beginning to realise that you are not going to recover very quickly. They may be finding the prospect of a member of their family being ill long-term a daunting one. They may find it almost impossible to accept that nothing can be done to make you better. As time passes it becomes clear that your GP, apart from issuing another sick note now and again, has little to offer you. Unable to accept that you may be ill for years, your family may start to act as if there is, in fact, a cure for ME out there; you have simply not been looking hard enough. They may refuse to allow you to wait and give your body a chance to heal naturally.

They find out about a doctor who has a 'special interest' in ME and urge you to see him. Your hopes are raised; perhaps this man will help you to get better. Not long into the appointment, however, you discover that this 'expert' knows less than you do about the disease. Worse still, he has several plans to tinker around with you, 'to see if it makes any difference' and proffers unconvincing theories to explain your continuing ill health; you hyperventilate, you are failing to take enough exercise, you need physiotherapy and so on. You leave feeling more undermined and uncertain about ME than before you came. But your family have more plans for you: they tell you stories they have heard about miraculous cures; the woman who completely recovered after having a baby, the man who got better by taking Hydrogen Peroxide. You feel dubious about these amazing recoveries and wonder why, if they are really genuine, they are not in the newspapers. Yet at the same time you feel that you owe it to your family – and perhaps even to yourself – to try absolutely anything, however bizarre, that claims to help just in case it works.

Although there may be members of your family who genuinely try to understand and go out of their way to help, there may be others who cannot seem to grasp what your illness is about. You try to educate them, you lend them leaflets and books advising how to help someone with ME. Yet, however much they read and however many times you explain they continue to say the wrong things to you and, furthermore, deny what living with ME is really like. They may find it hard to believe that one day you are able to do something and yet the day after the same thing makes you ill.

When you are too weak to get out of bed they say,

'Don't you think it would do you good to get up for a bit?'

When they ask how you are and you tell them you feel exhausted they reply,

'Yes, I feel terribly tired too... it must be the weather...' or, 'perhaps if you did a little exercise you might feel better...'

When you attempt to explain your anxieties about being ill they tell you that you do not really feel this way. You try to tell them your fear that you might never recover and they say,

'Well, don't worry, be positive, it might never happen.'

Even though your health might be deteriorating they refuse to allow you to try and face the worst,

'Come on', they say, 'you'll be better soon.'

When you cry with frustration and loneliness they tell you that they do not have that many friends either or that they do not go out as much as they would like. When you let off steam about how difficult you are finding it they remind you of situations that they deem far worse than yours,

'Think about the poor people in the world' they say, 'you must feel lucky to be in your nice warm bed with enough food to eat.'

Meanwhile your friendships are starting to be affected. Friends may find it hard to understand why you keep cancelling meetings with them and when you try to explain they may soon stop calling. The few that remain may feel ill at ease around you. What have they to talk to you about now that you are not working, going out for the evening or sharing the sort of life they lead? They may not understand why you are like this, 'but you don't *look* ill' they say. You try to tell them exactly what is wrong with you but end up feeling as if you are defending yourself. You feel they do not quite believe that ME is real, that they do not take it seriously,

'Isn't that the Yuppie Flu?' they joke, 'wouldn't mind lying around all day reading and watching TV myself.'

Your friends may expect your health to have improved since the last time you met and are confused if it has not. When you see each other you may be wary of mentioning your illness with them because you do not want to appear as if you are consumed by it, yet you feel cornered into explaining exactly the same things that you are sure you explained the last time you met. Even when you have told them, yet again, about your limitations they may act as if they have not heard. They may ask you what films you have seen at the cinema when you have told them that you cannot go out very often. They may ask about how your work is going when surely they know that you have been unable to work for nearly a year. It feels as if, all this time, you have been speaking in a language that they do not and seemingly cannot understand.

Why Family and Friends Deny

Why is it that family and friends deny the reality of your illness? They will almost certainly not be consciously aware of what they are doing. It is unlikely that they are deliberately going out of their way to make you miserable. Of course, there are always those who make themselves feel better by diminishing you, but in most cases people believe, if misguidedly, that they are helping you in some way with their comments and advice. If you told them that you are not comforted and that, in fact, you are made to feel considerably worse they would probably be very surprised. They may believe they are simply expressing their concern and, regardless of what you may tell them, will most likely continue to behave this way. Why should this be so?

First, your friends and relatives may genuinely feel anxious that you are not getting better. They may feel frustrated that, after all this time, you are still ill and that the illness imposes such limitations on your life. They may also feel irritated and angry that your illness makes demands on them and, therefore, affects their life. They may not be consciously aware of what motivates them to say undermining things to you, but their own feelings of impotence to change your, and therefore their own, situation certainly has something to do with it.

Second, your family and friends are unlikely to be familiar with serious illness in general and before you became ill may have had little or no experience of it. Before penicillin, it was not uncommon to know of someone in the community who was suffering from an illness necessitating long spells of convalescence. With poor living conditions, inadequate diets and wars that affected the entire population it was not uncommon for young and middle-aged people to be touched by death, disease and disablement. People were more used to seeing illness, it was part of everyday life. Becoming ill was not viewed as a personal failing, you simply had a disease amongst many diseases that no one knew a great deal about. Today all this has changed. Better living standards and advances in medicine have controlled many of the diseases that used to make invalids of people. Now many existing illnesses can be treated and the ill and the recovering are, if necessary, often moved out of the community into hospitals and residential homes.

The invisibility and separation of illness from the rest of the population means that you are likely to be the first long-term ill person your family and friends have ever met. They may have no experience of how to treat someone who is ill and, moreover, your situation may bring up all sorts of uncomfortable feelings that they may scarcely be able to deal with.

Until someone has personal experience of illness it is easy for them to see disease and misfortune as something that happens to other people. Before you became ill, many of those around you were able to distance themselves from illness; it had nothing to do with them. They could even blame the diseased, believing that they had brought it upon themselves. In our goal-orientated culture with its attitude that 'you can get it if you really want it', that you can control your own destiny, it is not difficult to believe that if you want it badly enough you can even overcome serious physical disease. There is no shortage of books explaining how, through a mixture of determination and 'positive thinking' you can avoid becoming ill. Or if you have 'made yourself' ill in the first place, how to heal yourself. The ideology that we can control not only our environment but also life itself, pervades Western society. We no longer believe that nature exists outside ourselves, that we are just another organism competing for survival alongside many others including bacteria and viruses that may well be more vigorous than we are. We no longer believe that fate and misfortune play any significant role in our lives. If only we can harness the correct attitude, develop the right knowledge, then we humans can control everything. We can fashion the life we want for ourselves, and those who fail to do so have only themselves to blame.

The fact that someone your family and friends know and are close to became ill poses a challenge to these ideas. They either have to completely change the way they view the sick and the unfortunate, thus accepting that you have simply been a victim of fate. Or they have to strengthen and consolidate their existing beliefs to continue to believe that people – including you – are generally responsible for their misfortune.

Whether they are aware of it or not, these ideas of human omnipotence and mastery over chance can help those who are close to you to lose sight of who you are; they allow your family and friends to view you as essentially different from them. They are able to believe that your ill-health is evidence of some, hitherto, unrecognised weakness in your personality.

These may not be conscious beliefs and will rarely, if ever, be openly stated yet the denial of the arbitrariness of disease, that it can happen to anybody; the denial that your illness has a physical cause rather than being stress-related; the belittlement of your symptoms and the lack of recognition of how well you are coping, effect you all the same.

People have an investment in, even subconsciously, believing these things. Your illness serves as a reminder of the capriciousness of life, it shows how uncertain and fragile life can be. It is a reminder that one day we will all, if not become ill, certainly die. These are painful and frightening thoughts. They are usually concealed very deeply inside a person and resist being disturbed. To accept that fate is able to deal you a blow, that it can turn your life upside down is a profound threat to many people. The terror of death and the fear of not being in control is unrivalled in most peoples' lives. Better to believe that disease only happens to certain groups in society, to respond to your becoming ill by blaming it on some personal weakness, on something you have or have not done. Easier to do this than admit that we do not, after all, live in a safe, dependable world and that we are all susceptible to tragedy and loss.

In this context, the way your family and friends react to your illness becomes clearer. Your words are difficult to hear because they threaten to undermine their safe view of the world. Even though they are unlikely to be aware of it, they try to control your experience of ME and attempt to silence your expression of it. Only by doing so can they maintain their feeling of security and stability.

2

Denial – Part Two

How denial affects you

When you develop a serious illness you hope for love, understanding and sympathy from those around you. It can be a terrible shock to encounter instead denial, ignorance and undermining. More than any other aspect of the disease it is this response from others that most troubles people with ME. The constant questioning about whether you are really ill, whether things are really that bad for you, the pressure to present a 'normal' appearance and hide your illness can sap the confidence of the most stoic sufferer. The refusal by others to accept the reality of ME is tantamount to refusing to accept you as a person. This is what makes denial so difficult to deal with.

When those close to you question the truth of your experience and treat your symptoms as merely an extension of your personality it undermines your ability to cope. You lose sight of who you are and with the erosion of your self-esteem you can begin to internalise how others see you. You may start to believe what they say is really true. If your doctor, family and friends, instead of admiring you for your courage and determination in living with a debilitating disease, treat you as if you are weak or even to blame for being ill you can soon feel isolated and estranged from the very people you most need to rely on.

Shame

Stigma has always attached itself to disease. Throughout the ages, people who have been seriously ill and disabled have been marked and have felt, as a result, a sense of shame about their affliction. In the past, the presence of disease was explained in religious terms, as reparation for past sins and so on. Although disease is no longer generally viewed as being a punishment from God there still remains a residue from this idea. The ill and disabled are still set apart, still made to feel more different than they are and at fault for not being healthy and 'whole'. Why this should occur in our supposedly civilised society is not entirely clear. Perhaps it is a throw-back to times when people cast out the diseased – the most well-known example being the leper – for fear of being infected. Although that risk is rarely present nowadays with chronic illness or disability in the western world, an unspoken fear and distaste of those afflicted still exists.

Certainly there are very few positive and attractive images of the long-term ill in our culture. Illness and disability are viewed as problems for which solutions must be found. This is nowhere more apparent than with genetic screening for foetal abnormalities and in the debates about genetic engineering. People naturally want their children to be born healthy. But where does one draw the line between the movement towards eradicating disease and disablement and the pursuit of absolute perfection? Of course, life is easier if you are well and able-bodied but the assumption that illness and disability has, at all costs, to be eliminated has inevitable repercussions for those who already find themselves in that position. The quest to rid our society of disease may be full of good intentions, but it can also be driven by unconscious prejudice against anyone who is different and therefore deemed unacceptable.

When you have a controversial disease such as ME the stigma can be more pronounced. It can feel embarrassing to 'admit' that you have the illness to people who may not believe that ME even exists or who think that you are suffering from a mental illness with delusions of being physically ill. Having to explain in the face of disbelief can almost make you feel that you have to apologise for having this disease in the first place. As a former doctor describes:

> I used to dread having to tell people what illness I had. I could almost hear them thinking, 'she's really lost her mind if she thinks she's got *that*'. It made me feel almost like lying to people when they asked what was wrong with me because I knew I would get a much more sympathetic response if I said I had a disease like MS.

Feeling ashamed to own your illness can be particularly painful when faced with a new and unsympathetic doctor. Many sufferers, in their quest for a diagnosis, encounter doctors who dismiss them for making a fuss over nothing. One virtually bed-bound woman was told by a visiting GP that she was, in fact, lucky to have ME:

> I couldn't believe my own ears when he said that. He went on to tell me that there were far worse diseases to have such as diabetes or arthritis. He continued to inform me that 'severity' in illness was purely subjective and that there were always people who considered themselves more incapacitated than others even though they were not. He implied that I should be ashamed of myself for lying in bed when I really didn't need to. That the only reason I was there was because I was less strong, more self-indulgent than others who, if I could just see it, were in a far worse situation than me. After he left I cried for ages. I felt as if he had stamped all over me. Up until then I had found it hard enough to cope but now I felt that my last bit of self-respect for how I was coping had been taken away.

The feeling of shame about having ME is compounded by its 'invisibility'. You may not outwardly appear that different from someone who is healthy. Having little or no energy can severely disable you but your disability may not immediately be apparent to the outside world. Others may not notice that, for someone who rests so much, you do not look very well. To them, you may look more or less 'normal' and they may find it difficult to believe that someone who looks this way can be seriously ill. Unfortunately, people's knowledge about illness is often limited. They expect someone who is seriously ill to look it and in the popular imagination that means looking as if you are actually dying; gaunt face, wasting body, thinning hair etc.. Likewise, they expect someone who is disabled to look as if they are disabled. Again, the word 'disabled' to most people means 'wheelchair-bound' – despite the fact that the majority of disabled people are not wheelchair users – or, at the very least, the use of a walking stick. Although using physical aids can be useful in the management of ME, there are many sufferers who do not find them suitable for their needs and yet are still very disabled by their illness. Some sufferers are so ill they would find it exhausting to go for a walk with a stick or even sit up in a wheelchair.

In reality, most people with chronic illness do not look that different from the rest of society. With ME you may be very pale and regardless of how much you rest have deep, dark circles under your eyes. But there are plenty of healthy people who can achieve a similar effect with a bad diet, heavy drinking and a few late nights! It can be hard to convince others that you are as ill as you say you are if you do not look as they would expect. Failing to conform to the popular conception of what it is to be ill or disabled can contribute to all kinds of awkwardness. One sufferer described his feelings about having to answer the door at midday in his pyjamas:

The postman was standing there and looked a bit taken aback that I wasn't dressed. 'On night shift then?' he asked. I couldn't bring myself to explain that I was long-term ill and yet I didn't want to lie so I just grunted in a non-committal way. Several weeks later I was, of course, still opening the door to the postman in my pyjamas and I could see that he was getting really curious. 'Got the flu have you?' This time I plucked up the courage and blurted out, 'Actually, I'm seriously ill' and grabbed my parcel before he had time to question me further. I felt humiliated to be having to answer the door in my dressing-gown when most people my age are out working. Because I probably don't look as if I am very ill I feel that the outside world sees me as lazy and weak; as if I want to be slobbing around in my pyjamas all day. I know I didn't choose to be ill but I can't help feeling slightly ashamed of being in this situation.

Self-Doubt

If your doctor fails to take your condition seriously, the seeds of doubt about your illness can be planted in your own mind. Your doctor may be someone in whom you have previously always placed your trust and even if you are given advice that you know will make you worse it is hard not to follow it. Even when doing so makes you quite obviously more ill, you may still be unable to completely reject what your doctor is telling you.

You can find yourself in a situation of knowing that certain things you do make you feel physically worse yet, at the same time, doubting it. Although you know it is nonsensical you can start torturing yourself about whether you really *are* ill or if you just *think* that you're ill. As one sufferer, a secretary now partly recovered, explained:

> My doctor told me I had ME but said that it was more my atti-tude to life that was making me ill rather than any actual disease. I don't know what he thought ME was. Perhaps he just used it as a convenient label for something he didn't know much about. He implied that my symptoms were a result of my not having – as he put it – a 'fighting attitude' to life. That made me so angry. But instead of taking my anger out on him, I took it out on myself. I started to question where my symp-toms came from and – I know this sounds quite mad – if I was 'really' feeling them at all. It's hard to explain but I lost all faith in my inner voice. I couldn't trust my own judgement about how I was feeling. I would go to work feeling terrible but push myself on and on until I could hardly get the bus home. I'd arrive back too ill to even eat and would have to go straight to bed. The exhaustion was overwhelming but I couldn't 'give in' to it. I was determined to have the 'right' attitude, to be a fighter and thought that if I carried on as if there was nothing wrong with me then things might get better. It sounds ridiculous now because it was obvious that my body was telling me something. I had been working full-time for years and now after a couple of days I'd feel half-dead. But I just refused to listen. All I could hear was my doctor saying that I could soon be better if only I changed my personality. He was wrong. Instead, I became increasingly ill until I not only had to give up work but could barely manage to look after myself.

Despite studies showing that the best recovery is made by those who are advised to stay within their limits and rest early on in the illness some doctors still believe that sufferers feel ill because they do not take enough exercise, that their weakness and exhaustion is from over-resting due to a fear of doing too much. The reality is quite the opposite. Most sufferers actually have a fear that they are doing too *little* and, even though they know it will make them feel worse, push their body well over its limit. If your doctor then tells you to do as much as you can regardless of how you feel, you are even more likely to disregard your limits and push yourself into severe disability.

Because there is such conflicting advice on how best to manage ME it can be impossible to feel sure that you are doing the right thing to improve your chances of recovery. There may be a growing body within orthodox medicine that takes the disease seriously and advises rest and avoidance of over-exertion as the best form of management but there are also myriad of other voices advising you to do completely the opposite. Scores of stories in self-help books and in the two ME charities' magazines relate how this person completely recovered after changing his diet or that person was cured by hypnotherapy. Many sufferers feel that they have found some relief through alternative therapy and there will always be those who believe that it has completely cured them. Yet there is a danger that such stories foster unrealistic expectations of recovery. Out of desperation to get better you may not be able to stop yourself from going from one therapy to another until you have tried absolutely everything – however unproven and risky – that makes a claim to help your symptoms. You may be seduced, despite your better judgement, into believing ever more extravagant claims that there is, after all, a cure for ME but that you are just not looking hard enough for it. When this 'cure' fails to materialise, your hopes can swiftly evaporate and turn instead to disillusionment and despair.

Magic thinking and Guilt

One of the most prevalent and psychologically damaging groups of 'therapies' are those based on the idea that you can get better simply by changing your personality. The high priests of this dogma base their ideas on the popular belief, discussed earlier, that you can completely control your own destiny. They proclaim that through the mind you can make anything happen; become slim, make a fortune and even cure yourself of terminal illness.

The initial attraction to these ideas may be due to there being a germ of truth in them. The connection between the mind and body has been known for some time. What goes on in your mind can affect your body. When you feel nervous your heart races, the palms of your hands become sweaty and your mouth turns dry. Most people recogise that stress and depression are capable of producing physical symptoms and can lower your resistance to illness. But this does not exclude the existence of a natural world outside that can invade the body and cause ill health. Countless thousands of children in developing countries, for example, die each year not because they feel anxious or depressed but because they live in extreme poverty that causes simple conditions like diarrhoea to become killers. Scientists have yet to unravel the considerable complexities which link the mind and body and good doctors do not attribute every illness which they know little about to the workings of the mind.

The practitioners of the various strands of 'mind-power' therapy do not, however, acknowledge such mundanities as bacteria or viruses. They believe that all ill health – from ME to AIDS – is the result of some inner psychological or spiritual conflict. Their ministry is based on an amalgam of magic and half-baked psychology packaged into an attractively simple, quasi-religious message that if you want it badly enough, you can heal yourself. They hook you in with an idea that seems reasonable enough, that when you feel positive you feel emotionally better and then persuade you that inside the mind lies a definitive cure. When you are seriously ill and there is no conventional cure available you want to believe that all you have to do to get better is to release your inner power.

For those who want to alter their lifestyle, change things that can be changed – lose weight, make new friends or learn to relax – there may be no serious harm to these ideas. But when applied to the seriously and chronically ill these ideas can be dangerous. By promising that the power of the mind can cure you, they raise false hopes of recovery and the effect of this can be devastating.

To suggest that sick and vulnerable people can be cured by simply thinking themselves well is cruel and irresponsible. Moreover, these ideas nourish a sense of guilt that many ill people – particularly those with ME – already feel. By promoting the idea that 'negative' thoughts are the cause of your ill health and only 'positive' thoughts can heal you they perpetuate the popular notion that the ill are to blame for their predicament. But the emotions it defines as negative; anger, jealousy, frustration and so on, are ones that are perfectly natural for those with long-term illness to experience. They are an entirely normal expression of loss and an integral part of coming to terms with a major life crisis. To advocate that the expression of such emotions is negative and that those who express them are so negative that they have not only made themselves ill but also prevented their own recovery is a complete denial of the reality of living with disease. The belief that you will only recover by filling your mind with sweet and positive thoughts arises out of and sustains a culture that shies away from the expression of pain and suffering, a culture where those who find themselves victim to misfortune are shunned and stigmatised.

The idea that you can heal yourself by changing your attitude or by trying just that little bit harder to get better may have a familiar ring to many people with ME. You are more than likely to have heard that message, perhaps in a more diluted, less overt manner from your family and friends and even your doctor. If you hear this over and over again it is not surprising that you begin to believe it. You may start to think that, perhaps, you do have the power to make yourself well again, that if you just change certain aspects of your personality you will get better. You may decide to try and follow this 'mind-over-matter' philosophy but find that you cannot help feeling 'negative' thoughts. You may start to feel guilty and a failure for continuing to be ill and internalise the idea that recovery is eluding you because you are not trying hard enough. The alluring promise that you can make yourself better by teaching your mind to think only positive thoughts may quickly turn sour when, despite following the teachings of this so-called 'therapy', you show no signs of improvement. You can soon find yourself in a downward spiral of feeling guilty for being ill, feeling that you are such a negative and bitter person that it is your fault that you cannot make yourself well again.

Dealing with Denial

The first step in dealing with denial is to recognise that it is happening. Initially you may not even be aware of the role denial plays in your feelings of uncertainty and insecurity about ME; you may believe that they simply come from within yourself. To begin to deal with these feelings you have first to recognise that many of them are in response to pressures from outside. Once you realise this you will be better able to see where these pressures are coming from. You can then start to sift through the comments that keep you feeling anxious and self-doubting and, at last, develop some self-preservation.

You may not be able to change other people's antagonistic or undermining attitudes towards you but you can refuse to listen to them. By distancing yourself from people who make you feel worse, you cease to allow what other people think to dominate your life. Instead of keeping the company of those who will never be understanding or sympathetic, try to meet people who will empathise with your situation. Get in touch with other sufferers in your area through your local group or via the various special interest groups run by the two ME charities. (See Appendix for details). By surrounding yourself with people who accept your illness – and therefore accept you – you will begin to feel more secure within yourself. By keeping at arms length those who are ignorant and dismissive, you will no longer feel so tortured within yourself about your illness. Cutting out antagonism and developing nourishing contacts will allow you to develop more confidence in yourself and your ability to trust what your body is telling you.

Of course, it is not always easy to distance yourself from those who make life more difficult, particularly as they may be the very people to whom you look for support. But in many cases you can still maintain a relationship so long as you are very firm that you will no longer tolerate undermining or diminishing comments. For your own peace of mind you have to try to put your foot down and listen only to those who encourage and help you. Instead of giving attention to other people's, often uninformed, opinions about how you should be living your life you need to develop some self-reliance. This can be difficult when you are feeling physically and emotionally low. But until you begin to develop a sense of self-protection and belief in your own knowledge of what is good for you, you will never be able to move on and begin to accept your situation.

It can be very tricky challenging family and friends about their hurtful comments as they will undoubtedly be unaware of their effect on you. By arguing your case you can swiftly get embroiled in a quarrel and end up explaining and defending your position. They may not understand why you get so wound up by what they say. If you then become justifiably angry you risk damaging your relationship – particularly if the other party cannot understand what you are getting angry about. Often, the most effective way of dealing with damaging comments is to avoid picking up the cues that others provide in the first place. By ignoring them and changing the subject you can move the conversation away from potential conflict.

Another approach is to confront the person in question directly and tell them unequivocally that you do not wish to discuss the matter further. Do not try to explain why or get drawn into a discussion about it. Be firm and assertive, repeating your request over and over again, until they have got your message. Say something like, 'let's not talk about illness any more' or, 'I'd really prefer not to talk about it, I'd much rather hear what you've been doing lately' and so on. You can practise saying these sorts of things to yourself until you feel comfortable asserting yourself. (See Appendix: *Useful Books* on learning to be assertive.)

The third way of dealing with denying friends or relatives is the most drastic and should only be attempted if you are absolutely sure that the relationship is really harming your self-esteem and has no chance of improving. This is temporarily to cut out a person who is making your life unbearable until you feel stronger within yourself. It can be painful to do this but you have to decide which is the better of two evils. A good half-way measure is to change the type of communication you have with that person. Rather than seeing them face to face you can occasionally phone instead. Or if you have a phone relationship, you can convert this into keeping in touch through letters. This way you can limit your exposure to the offending person while still maintaining contact.

The most important lesson to learn is that you do have some control over what messages you allow to enter and influence your life. You must exercise this control if you do not want to waste any of the precious energy you need to manage your illness. You cannot afford to maintain relationships which hamper your ability to cope.

In the same way, if you find that you are not getting the support you need from your GP you must try and get together and have a frank talk about it. You may feel anxious that other diseases have not adequately been ruled out or have worries that you are not being taken seriously. If so, try and pluck up the courage to tell your doctor how you feel. If it helps, take with you a sympathetic friend or relative for moral support but do ask the questions that need to be asked even if you think you might appear foolish or – as many ME sufferers fear – a hypochondriac. It is your doctor's job to reassure you about any health worries you may have.

Realistically, people with ME often settle for a less than perfect relationship with their doctor because they are aware – either from their own or other's experience – of the potential to be treated even worse by other GPs. Until the medical profession is educated about ME and receives proper training on how to listen and support patients, you may have to accept a service that only meets your very basic needs. If you have tried to educate your doctor (see Appendix for where to obtain suitable information) and yet s/he still dismisses you it may be time to find another one. Your local group or one of the ME charities will point you in the right direction. You may not get all the help and sympathy you need from your GP but the least you should expect is to be met with a degree of civility and care.

It can be very hard to believe in yourself and act assertively with your doctor especially when you are feeling unwell but it is important, if you can face it, to protest if you are mistreated in any way. Even if you cannot bring yourself to say anything at the time it is still worth making a stand in the form, perhaps, of a letter of complaint. This will show – at the very least to yourself – that you will not tolerate being dismissed or abused. (See Chapter Six on making a complaint about a GP.) It is easier said than done, but when you begin to define certain behaviour as unacceptable and to really believe that you deserve to be treated with courtesy and respect, you will find that your self-esteem feels less shaky. When you deny others the opportunity to put you down you begin to feel less under attack and less likely to be crippled with self-doubt. From this position of strength you will be more able to start accepting your illness.

When you are besieged with feelings of shame tell yourself – in the mirror if necessary – that you having nothing to be ashamed of that, regardless of what others may think, you have not chosen to be ill and you are doing your very best to cope with an extremely difficult situation. Pat yourself on the back for doing so well. You have a special reason for holding your head high because of your courage and determination in living each and every day with such a challenging disease as ME

When you are plagued with feelings of guilt try to recognise where they are coming from. Perhaps someone has said something to you, implied that you are not coping well or put pressure on you to behave in a certain way. Try very hard not to internalise other peoples' ideas or feelings about your illness. Remember that when those around you feel a bit guilty themselves – perhaps because they know that they are not doing enough to help you – they may instead of acknowledging these feelings pass them on to you. Remind yourself that you are the expert on your illness and only you know how hard it can be. By all means accept informed advice from others, remain open-minded about alternative therapies but keep a firm hold on your inner sense of what is right for you. Trust your instincts and listen first to yourself and second to others.

Finally, accept that even when you have done all these things and find that you are less affected by denial and more self-confident and secure in yourself there may always be some comment that opens up the wounds again. However close you are to accepting your situation, just one tactless remark can bring back all those tormenting feelings of self-doubt and insecurity. This time round, however, the effect will be short-lived – maybe a day, maybe a few hours – because you have done the ground work. It will take a little time to find your feet again, but you will know that you have built the solid foundation on which your self-esteem now stands and that by coming to terms with denial you have really begun the journey towards acceptance.

3

Anger

Anger can creep up on you surreptitiously so that you are hardly aware of its effect on your life or it can hit you with great waves of frustration, envy, irritation and rage against yourself, your illness and everyone around you. You may not know why you have these feelings or where they come from – you might not even be aware that what you are feeling *is* anger – and the strength of your emotions may be so overwhelming that you simply do not know what to do with them. You may feel inadequate and blame yourself for having such unpleasant feelings and then be thrown into confusion when, as suddenly as they came, they disappear and are replaced with a sense of relative calm.

One of the great fables in our culture is that the ill and disabled fall into two groups: the 'happy cripple'; smiling and serene, bravely fighting disease and misfortune without complaint and the 'bitter invalid'; cynical and self-pitying, unable to accept their lot with any grace or equanimity. Brought up with this myth, it can feel shameful even to admit to feeling angry or jealous or frustrated. These emotions can seem distasteful to those around you and even to yourself, their presence a confirmation of a personality too self-indulgent to beat the illness, too embittered to accept it. In a society which tacitly discourages the open expression of pain, it can seem unacceptable to even feel such taboo emotions as disaffection and rage.

You are unlikely to feel a great deal of anger until you have dealt with denial. Only when you accept that you are really ill will you then be able to fathom the devastation ME has wreaked on your life. While you may not have dreamed of asking, 'why me?' through the first months or even years of your illness, now you may not be able to get the question out of your mind; 'Why is life so unfair?' you ask yourself. Perhaps for the first time you see the injustice of all the disbelief, the stigma and discrimination that you have had to endure. Now that you accept ME as a real part of your life, you see more clearly the chaos and damage it has brought with it. You look back and see how your life was and what you have lost, you look forward and see how your life looks now with, possibly, no work, few friends and little independence. You start to compare yourself with those around you and passively watch them do the things you used to – and they still do – take for granted. You want to explode with the frustration of living each and every day with a disease that robs you of the very essence of life; energy.

Anger turned outwards; Rage

The most straightforward kind of anger comes in dramatic bursts of rage, storms of emotion that unexpectedly gush forth when you are almost at breaking point. Perhaps for months you have listened politely to ignorant comments about ME until, one day, you find that you cannot listen to another word. The next person who tells you how well you look is met with a tirade of exasperation and fury that has been held in for the last six months.

You may think you are feeling relatively calm as you lay the table for dinner or take a dish out of the cupboard then, suddenly, you drop a plate and as it smashes to the floor your patience snaps. That single act of clumsiness flings open the door on all the frustration and rage just waiting to be let out as expressively and forcibly as possible. One sufferer was shocked to find out the strength of her anger:

> My husband and I were having an argument – about the most trivial of things – and suddenly something inside me snapped. I'd been cutting some bread and I had this knife in my hands and just started crying and stabbing the breadboard with tears of frustration. My poor husband didn't know what had come over me. There was never any danger of me attacking anything but the board but how could he know that? Afterwards, I felt terrible about acting like that but, in a way, it helped get all my pent-up frustration out into the open.

If strong emotions cannot find an outlet verbally or physically they will often find expression in the fantasy world of nightmares and daydreams. One bedbound sufferer, often disturbed by noisy neighbours, spoke of her daydreams:

When they start making the usual racket I get so mad because there's not a single thing I can do about it. My carer has asked countless times if they can keep it down a bit but they take absolutely no notice. I'll be lying there listening to the noise and the most violent fantasies just seem to pop into my head. I've always loathed violence and wouldn't have the energy to carry out anything even if I wanted to but just imagining my selfish neighbours coming to a sticky end so they'll never disturb me again gives me, at least, some sort of release.

Anger also expresses itself more subtly and in such a way that you may not even recognise your feelings as having anything to do with anger at all. This can occur especially if you have always found it difficult to express your emotions. Instead of sudden outbursts of rage you may experience increasing feelings of irritability. This low grade irritability may occasionally provoke you to snap at those close to you but more often it becomes sublimated into certain kinds of behaviour. You may, for example, feel an almost obsessive urge to do something such as sort out a cupboard, polish some shoes or, like one sufferer – who was always quite laid back about housework before she got ill – clean the kitchen and tidy up the house. Feeling compelled to take control of your environment as a means of expressing your irritation and the submerged anger towards your situation can, unfortunately, leave you feeling even more irritable than when you started. Having ME, you are unlikely to be well enough to carry out the tasks that you feel you need to do and even if you are able to complete them to your satisfaction you will probably become anxious and frustrated when things get messy again. The displacement of feelings of impotence and rage into a compulsion to tidy or clean, or to pursue any activity in an obsessive manner, can only leave you feeling even less in control and hence more frustrated as you find yourself driven by impulses you cannot keep in check.

Anger turned inwards; Bargaining and Self-Blame

Whereas anger turned outwards can show itself as rage, irritability and even obsessive behaviour, anger turned inwards often results in self-blame and self-denigration. First, you may start a process of bargaining, appealing to God, Nature or any other mighty force to be spared some of the worst aspects of the illness. You promise to try and become a better person, more religious, nicer to your family if only you could, please, recover and soon. More desperate, you may say things like, 'Look, I don't mind if I have to be ill for another year or so, but please, let me get better after that.' The more ill you are the lower your expectations, 'Okay, I don't mind being house-bound and in bed most of the time, but please let me not have to be in such sickness and pain.'

When your pleas are ignored you start bargaining with your body, 'If you just allow me to continue working part-time then I won't get too angry'. But when your body fails to cooperate, the bargaining and cajoling soon grind to a halt. Your frustration turns inwards in the form of self-loathing and disgust. Now you may find yourself saying, 'Okay you useless lump of flesh, you won't let me work, you won't let me have any social life, at least get me to the shops and back or else…' Soon you may be attacking not only your body for being unable to do things, but yourself. When you have a relapse – even though it may be entirely unrelated to anything that you have done – you chastise yourself for being so stupid as to have overdone it. As one teenager explains:

> I shout and swear at myself all the time. If my health goes downhill after going out I blame myself and tell myself what an idiot I am for overdoing it. I suppose I'm my worst tormentor but I've got to take out my frustration on someone and if there's no one else around, I guess, that someone's got to be me.

Society's tendency to 'blame the victim' facilitates the turning of anger against yourself. It is also easier to blame yourself for being ill or for not getting better when you live against a back-drop of denial about ME. If you get into the habit, however, of blaming yourself for your illness there is a real danger that you may start to believe that being ill is some sort of punishment for not being a good enough person. There are many people who believe that their illness has been sent to teach them a lesson and that, somehow, they deserve to be ill. Once you start believing that having ME is your fault, your self-esteem is in real trouble. Attacking and blaming yourself not only eats

away at your self-worth but also encourages you to see yourself as so many others may see you; as nothing but illness. By
keeping up the onslaught of abuse against yourself, you allow
the disease to pervade every crevice of your personality. You
become what you are battling against; a person entirely
consumed and defined by illness.

Frustration

ME is an especially frustrating disease. Its fluctuating character
means that from one day, and even one hour, to the next you
can never know how you will feel. On top of this there is the
uncertainty of having an illness that nobody knows much
about. For all you know you may get better, you may get worse
or you may stay at the same level for years. From the very
beginning you have no idea if you will be ill for just six months
or so or for the rest of your life. You may or may not be told
that you have a greater chance of recovery in the early years of
the disease but you will most certainly be bombarded with
conflicting messages about the best way to manage ME, resulting in more frustration as you go from pillar to post searching
for that elusive cure.

From day to day, particularly for the more severely affected,
ordinary planning becomes an obstacle course. You might
accept a social invitation but when the day arrives you may
not be well enough to go. Even if you make an appointment
that very day, within an hour or even by the time you have got
washed and dressed, you may feel too ill to keep it. The fickle
nature of ME makes it impossible to think ahead with any
certainty and robs you of control over your life.

This inability to make plans for even the immediate future is
what makes ME so especially frustrating to live with. When
your life has been torn apart by illness and you are left with
very little energy, you need to be able to arrange things to look
forward to; a trip to the park, a meeting with a friend, anything
to make the time pass more pleasantly. Yet because you never
know if you are going to feel well enough on a particular day,
the benefit of the anticipation of doing something enjoyable –
or even getting something routine out of the way – is tarnished
by the ever-present anxiety over whether or not you are going
to be able to make it.

This unpredictability also puts a pressure on relationships with those on whom you rely. If you are habitually having to change your plans, you are inevitably going to mess up the arrangements of those who have volunteered to take you out, and you may soon find that the offers begin to dry up. Even if you are able to go out, you are perpetually aware that at any moment you may be overcome with nausea and fatigue. You can never tell when your last bit of energy will run out, if the next step will be the last one before you have to be rushed home to lie down. Or, as one man with ME whose partner also has the disease explains, you might feel up to a short outing but cannot go out because of other considerations:

Often when one of us feels well enough to go out the other doesn't. It's exasperating because I'm only up to going out occasionally but when I am, my partner – who's the driver – often isn't up to it herself. I don't like taxis as, apart from the cost, I don't know how long my energy is going to last which creates problems ordering a taxi for my return. Besides, I need the reassurance of someone with me in case I feel ill and have to get home quickly. There is a local disability transport scheme but they're unsuitable as you need to book them in advance and I never know until the last minute if I'm well enough to go out. So the few times when I do feel fit enough to get out of the house I'm left stuck at home climbing the wall in frustration.

Even if you are able to overcome such obstacles and manage to do something, the knowledge that you will more than likely have to pay for it later casts a shadow over your enjoyment. Not everyone with ME is so restricted but for many this is one of the most frustrating aspects of the illness. You can be so careful not to overdo it when you get the opportunity for some activity yet, more often than not, end up suffering for your tiny taste of freedom and normality. A few hours (or if you are a little better, a day or so) later you start to feel more exhausted and sick than usual with pains in the legs and so on. You compare what you used to be able to do with what you can do now and feel frustrated with the illness for disabling you so. You chafe against the unfairness of feeling worse after doing so little and feel annoyed with yourself that you did anything to make you feel this bad. Yet, at the same time, you know that you have to go out sometimes simply to maintain your sanity.

The continual calculations that need to be made in order to manage any activity; if I want to keep this appointment then I'll have to stay in bed the day before; if I want to see this friend I'll have to put off going to the shops, can wear the patience of the most stalwart of sufferers. And there is little let up; the same calculations may have to be made day in day out, week after week, year after year. Seeing things that you want to do remain just beyond your reach or being well enough to do something one day and yet unable to do the same the next can be maddening. And the occasions when you do manage to go out or finish some task can remind you all the more how disabled you are the majority of the time.

If it feels frustrating to be unable to go out and do the things that you used to, then it is doubly frustrating when the quality of the life you are left with is so low. Many sufferers not only have to deal with being disabled but also with feeling physically sick, weak and in pain each day. More frustrating still is that just when you feel you have enough health problems, a new symptom can suddenly crop up for you to deal with. One sufferer, a student, found that his incessant stomach problems on top of all his other ME symptoms were the final straw:

> I was getting hopeful about returning to college as I was beginning to feel a little stronger when I got these awful stomach problems that I've never had before. It really set me back and now I'm worse than ever. If only my stomach would improve I'm sure I'd be back to feeling a bit better again and maybe move forward. It's so frustrating having to have this as well as my other symptoms. It's just another thing to have to cope with.

Although some people feel that they have found relief through alternative therapies, the bottom line for many sufferers is that there is little they can do – beyond sensible rest and a healthy diet – except wait for their symptoms to recede. This waiting and the feeling of powerlessness that accompanies it is perhaps the most fundamentally frustrating experience of all. Having to put up with ME patiently, without knowing how long it is going to take to get better is a prison sentence of the worst kind. The open-endedness of a disease with no 'release date', no firm prognosis to hang on to demands the most extreme patience.

Jealousy

Jealousy can be very painful. It not only eats you up inside and can make life seem unbearable but you can also feel terribly guilty for even experiencing an emotion that is so often frowned upon. Although jealousy, and by extension those who show it, are often characterised as ugly and unpleasant it is quite natural in the context of chronic illness to have these feelings. Jealousy normally stems from a sense of insecurity and low self-esteem – the very feelings that are almost impossible to avoid at some stage with ME. Being ill can make you feel unattractive and undesirable so it is hardly surprising that when your well partner, for example, is still able to go out into the world looking great while you are sloping about the house all day in your pyjamas you may feel a little insecure. You may start to wonder how s/he can possibly avoid meeting some healthy person who would be much better for them than an invalid like yourself. The basic inequality in the carer/patient role, while not being easy for the carer, often contributes to anxiety and a lack of self-worth in the person being cared for. This differential can soon lead to feelings of jealousy as one severely affected man explains:

> Each time my wife goes out I get quite worked up. It's not that I really think she's going to have an affair, it's just that I convince myself that she can't wait to get out of the house and away from me and what I represent: illness, depression, neediness and that she has a marvellous time with all sorts of people in all sorts of situations of which I have no part. I do feel jealous that she might prefer to be with these people rather than me. I also admit that I envy her being able to go out and socialise while I'm stuck here in bed all day. And, of course, what carer doesn't look forward to having a break from 'the invalid'? I'm sure my wife does have a good time when she's away from me. I know it's doing her good, but I still find it very hard.

If you had to compete for love or attention as a child your attacks of jealousy may be more severe. Yet whatever your childhood, it is very common to feel some pangs of envy when you are prevented, through illness, from participating in the things that everyone around you is doing. A situation is always more difficult to bear when you feel you are the only one suffering. Throughout the Second World War, for example, people put up with hardships such as food shortages and bombings because they knew everyone else was in the same, or considerably worse, situation. What caused tremendous resentment and jealousy, however, were families who because of their wealth or social position were able to override the restrictions of rationing by buying food on the black market or could arrange safe posts for their sons. Knowing that such unfairness existed made it that much more difficult for people to cope with their difficulties.

In the same way, being ill in a largely healthy society makes coping with long-term illness that much harder. The fitness and good fortune of others act as salt in your wounds. All around you, people are getting on with their lives while you struggle with the remnants left by ME. When you switch on the television, read the paper, nod to your neighbour, see your family or friends, their full lives bear heavily down on the emptiness of your own. How can you not feel envious when you look out of the window and see people going to work or going out with friends while all you can do is watch as your life seems to slip by? How can you help feeling jealous of others' achievements and happiness?

Because you are surrounded by people who are generally better off than you it can feel like torture just to get through the day. Unless you live on a desert island, everything and everyone you come into contact with can remind you of what you have lost. Of course, everyone has their problems and even though you may think that your neighbours or friends are perfectly content they may well be hiding great pain behind that happy facade. Yet other people's problems are often not as severe as your own. They may be out of work or facing divorce or feel lonely but the ME sufferer is likely to have all these problems as well as a good many more. As one sufferer put it:

> I never thought that I would end up envying other people's problems! Now I can hardly bear to hear about them because I can't help feeling, 'Oh, if only I had *that* kind of worry'.

It can be difficult not to feel jealous of the attention given, in the media and by those around you, to difficulties such as unemployment, single parenthood or, even, other diseases which are taken more seriously than ME. Behind this jealousy is often a great need to have the tremendous difficulties that you face properly acknowledged and accepted.

The Roots of Anger

You may not at first realise why you are feeling so angry and irritable all the time. When you are busy denying that you are really ill or blaming yourself for your predicament the real and valid reasons for feeling anger can easily be obscured. If your GP, family or friends fail to take your illness seriously it can be easy to inadvertently adopt their attitude that things are not really that bad so what have you got to complain or be angry about? When you continue to experience feelings of anger you can then enter a self-destructive cycle of feeling guilty for having these emotions and blaming yourself even more.

When you become ill, people tend to treat you differently from the way they used to. It is as if now that you have less control over your life you do not deserve to be treated quite like an adult. All of a sudden your family and friends may be contradicting you, telling you that you do not really feel the way you do or that you do not really want to do what you say you want to do. They may no longer listen to your point of view nor believe that what you have to say is valid or of interest. Becoming ill can deprive you of the status you used to hold within the family and your position may be relegated to that of a child whose daily life is dictated by others. You may find that when meeting people, they see only your illness and not you as a person. In their eyes you have almost lost some of what it is to be human; you are no longer quite like them.

People you do not even know suddenly feel that they can ask you personal questions, details about your life that if you had met them when you were well and on an equal footing they would never have dared to ask. Now that you are ill, and especially with a 'controversial' disease like ME, people do not just ask but *demand* to know the most intimate details of your symptoms; how you know that it is not merely psychosomatic, how far exactly can you walk, have you really tried to get better and so on. One sufferer, when asked by a neighbour what he did for a living, told him that he was ill and was

promptly asked, 'Well how do you manage to live then?'
Somehow, now that you are ill, it is deemed acceptable to ask
such personal questions because, after all, you are only an
invalid.

When you become ill you are often put into a position where
other people have power over you. You may have previously
led a completely independent life, earning your own living,
making your own decisions, choosing the people you wished
to see. Now you may find yourself in the care of someone else,
someone who, however kind and well-meaning, fits you into
their schedule. Because you may have to rely on someone else,
a carer or a home help, to help you with your basic needs or to
take you out and so on, you no longer have complete control
over what you do and when. Now you are obliged to see
people you may not want to see. It is likely that you will have
to listen to doctors who do not believe that ME exists or others
who have their own theories about the disease and how to
manage it. Suddenly, there are all these people involved in your
previously private life, all with an opinion on how you should
be running it.

Because of your physical limitations you have little choice
but to relinquish some of your personal power and rely on
others. But sometimes the power that others hold can be
abused. Knowing that an injustice has been done and yet feeling too physically weak to prevent it can lead to intense
feelings of rage against not only those who abuse your vulnerability but also against your illness for forcing you into a
situation in which you cannot properly defend yourself.

Your doctor, for example, decides whether or not you are ill
enough to claim Incapacity and other Disability Benefits.
Without your doctor's support you can find yourself in real
financial straits. Your doctor has the power to decide what
treatments should be made available to you and without his
or her referral you may not have access to therapies that might
be beneficial. If you are unlucky enough to have a doctor who
does not believe that you are really ill you may be forced to
continue to work until you drive yourself into severe disability.
Your doctor may deem that you have been on benefit for too
long and – even if the evidence shows that you are still very ill
– stop issuing sick notes leaving you in the impossible and
dangerous position of having to find work when you are not
physically up to it. Even if you are being issued sick notes your

doctor may be so generally undermining and dismissive of your condition that you may start to believe that you do not deserve any help and feel angry at yourself for being so 'pathetic' as to have to depend on the welfare state.

There are many other situations that encourage you to feel that you do not deserve the assistance that other disabled people get and it is right that you should feel angry about this. You may have to attend an assessment to determine your eligibility for a particular Benefit and be met with such suspicion and lack of respect that when your claim is denied you can hardly face the possibility of going through it all again at a review or tribunal. Or you may apply for an orange badge because you find walking very painful but are told that you cannot be that disabled because you managed the stairs on your way up to the assessment centre and so obviously have no need for a badge at all.

Of course you feel angry when you have to face this kind of ignorance and discrimination from people who should know better. Of course you should feel enraged about consistently being refused help just because you are unlucky enough to have a disease whose symptoms are misunderstood or dismissed. It can make you feel even more frustrated and angry when you know that there are people with lesser, but more visible, disabilities who receive the benefits that you are denied despite their leading far more active lives.

With an illness like ME it is hard not to learn to expect ignorance and prejudice; from the house-bound library service volunteer who greets you with, 'Well, you can't need this service, you don't look ill at all!' to the neighbour who, when you tell them you have ME, looks you straight in the eye and asks, 'But how do you *know* you're ill?' However used to such comments you become it can still be very difficult not to get angry about them.

How Others React to Anger

Most people find anger difficult to listen to. This is understandable and it is hard when faced with someone's rage and frustration not to take it personally. Your family and friends may interpret your generalised anger towards your situation as a direct attack on them. They may misinterpret your frustration about having to explain, yet again, about ME – and the defensiveness that inevitably accompanies this seemingly endless explaining of your life – as anger.

It takes a lot of patience and empathy to realise that an angry person is usually someone who is very unhappy inside and who desperately needs to be listened to and understood. In general, people are frightened and put off by expressions of anger. Your rage and disillusionment can bring up feelings, perhaps anger that they themselves have locked up inside, that they may prefer to keep in check. By accepting your anger and pain as justified, those close to you have to acknowledge how difficult your circumstances are. By making this acknowledgment they come face-to-face with what your life is like and what, if any, contribution they are going to make to help improve it. Often people do not want to make the changes necessary to make such a contribution, however small, to the lives of those less fortunate than themselves. We no longer live in a society in which duty plays much of a role. Increasingly, people look to the state to look after the old, the sick and the disabled even when the state is not, and can never be, a completely adequate provider. Denying that you have any valid reason to be angry, and casting you in the role of a bitter complainer in no real need of help, is a convenient way of letting some family members and friends off the hook. By ignoring your anger, trivialising your reasons for it and implying that you should not feel this way, it is a lot easier to turn their back on your cries for help.

When you are ill, there is an enormous pressure to conform to the stereotype, mentioned earlier, of the cheerful, positive invalid. You are rewarded if you project a normal, happy face; you receive encouraging statements about how well you are coping, affirmations and praise for being optimistic. If, on the other hand, you fail to appear this way and are sometimes honest about how it really is, you are punished; people withdraw, give you the cold shoulder, shake their heads in silent reproach.

If you stray from your assigned role you risk hearing how 'concerned' everyone is that you are allowing your illness to get the better of you, or how 'worried' people are that you are letting yourself become terribly over-sensitive and bitter. You may be subjected to pointed fables about how marvellous these people are who are *completely paralysed* and yet still manage to face life with such geniality and good humour, or how *awful* it must be for people who are *so disabled* that they cannot even wipe away their own tears. These stories are a backhanded response to your expressions of anger. Their message is that you should keep quiet about how you feel because, after all, there are people in far worse situations than you and that it is rather shameful to complain about your life when it is not nearly so bad.

Dealing with Anger

To deal with anger you first have to recognise that it is actually happening. To be able to do something about it, you have to see your outbursts of frustration or jealousy or self-blame for what they are. Only when you realise and accept that what you are feeling is anger will you be in the position to analyse where your anger comes from, understand the reasons behind it and start to deal constructively with it.

The first hurdle is to stop directing your anger against yourself. You must try to believe that becoming ill was not your fault. You never asked to get ME and now that you have it you must try to accept that, apart from sensible management, there is not much more you can do to influence its progress. It gets you nowhere to chastise yourself for being in a situation not of your own making. You cannot help being ill, but being ill is not the only thing that you are. It may feel as if ME has taken over your entire life, and its stanglehold on you can make you want to attack yourself in impotent rage. Yet, if you search you will find a tiny part of yourself that this illness has not claimed for itself. You will see that it is something that has happened to your body, but it does not have to completely define what and who you are.

By distancing yourself from your illness, by seeing it for what it is; an uninvited guest which has long outstayed its visit, you can see that you are not just illness. ME is something separate from you, something that has come unbidden into your life. However ill you are, you are still a person in your own right with the power to improve, if not your health, the way you cope with your new life.

When you are able to recognise this you can stop berating yourself for being ill and start making your life more bearable.

You can stop punishing yourself for not getting better and start accepting that you are doing your best to cope with an especially difficult and frustrating disease.

When you have removed yourself as the target of your anger you will see much more clearly which particular situations make you angry. You will also be in a better position to recognise those people who especially wind you up. Identifying the source of your anger will enable you to express your feelings when you need to and deal with the scenarios that make you most angry.

First you must accept that feeling angry does not mean that you are bitter or twisted. You do not have to feel guilty or ashamed for experiencing what are, after all, wretched and painful emotions that nobody would deliberately choose to have. Tell yourself that you do not wish to feel this way but seeing that, at the present time you do, there is no need to beat yourself up about it. Remind yourself that these emotions are a natural part of the grieving process and that, far from being negative, their expression is actually a positive way of coming to terms with chronic illness.

It is very important to find an appropriate outlet for your feelings. You need to find someone with whom you can express exactly how you feel without fear of judgement or reproach. Your family or friends may not always be the best people to pour out all your frustration and anger to, unless they are particularly understanding and insightful. And even if one of them is able to listen and respond in a helpful way their very closeness to you means that, if time goes on and you remain ill, their patience may wear thin and they will suffer 'burn-out'.

The best solution is to find a counsellor, someone who is trained to help people come to terms with painful and burdensome feelings. You need to be able to let out freely and, if necessary, on a long-term basis, the build up of tensions and resentments that inevitably ferment when living with ME. You need to talk of the unfairness you have suffered, the stigma of being ill, the lack of sympathy and understanding you have encountered, your feelings of powerlessness and the sickness and pain you have to endure. You need to have your anger validated, be reassured that you do not just have a chip on your shoulder but have a right and a reason to feel the way that you do. It is not always easy to find a suitable counsellor who has experience or, at least, an awareness of the problems of being ill. (See Chapter Six: *'Medical Matters'* for advice on how to find someone who is right for you.) If you know that each week you have the opportunity and space to let out all your frustration, envy and rage, you will find that these feelings, having found some release, will diminish.

If you are unable or do not wish to see a counsellor there are other self-help ways of releasing some of your anger. Choose a time each day or at least once a week when you allow yourself to vent some of your feelings. Rather than taking it out on unwilling relatives or friends take a cushion and beat it as hard as your energy will allow. Physically punching something inanimate is remarkably therapeutic and helps get out pent-up frustration. While doing this you may find yourself able to cry and shout in a way that you may have been unable to previously. Alternatively, take a piece of paper and write down how you feel. Do not allow yourself to be critical or self-conscious about what you write but simply let the first words that come into your mind flow out. You can also write letters to the people who you feel have mistreated you. Really let out all your feeling and resentment and write down exactly what you think of them. When you have finished, make a ceremony out of destroying your letter. Rip it into tiny shreds or even set it alight and watch it burn away.

If words do not come easily to you and you feel up to it, get some coloured pencils, children's crayons or even a couple of biros in different colours and draw anything that comes into your head. Do not think about or analyse what you are doing. Even if you believe that you are no good at drawing it does not matter – your picture is not going to be seen by anyone or displayed on a museum wall. Try to move your hand freely over the paper, making as much mess as you like. Express how you feel through colour as well as movement. Remember not to stop to assess what you are doing. Often this type of drawing can be even more effective than talking in relieving feelings of anger.

When people treat you badly or with less respect because you are ill, do your best to challenge them at the time. If you can manage to assert yourself there and then you are less likely to feel angry about it afterwards. Constantly remind yourself that though you may be ill and isolated, though you may be unable to work and, by society's standards, no longer hold much status, you are still as deserving of respect as any other human being. If the same people continue to mistreat you, the decision is going to have to be made about whether it is really beneficial for you to go on seeing them. At the very least, if you want to avoid confronting them, you can always say that you feel too ill to carry on talking. This way you can, with relative ease, get out of a particularly destructive conversation. If people insist on asking pointed personal questions you have every right to change the subject or – and this will fox them completely – simply ignore their questions altogether.

You have to learn to stick up for yourself and although this is difficult when you feel ill and vulnerable, you are less likely to be abused if you show yourself strong and still in control.

Although it can be extremely vexing, try to be patient with those close to you. Some of them may genuinely, in their ignorance, believe they are helping you with their comments. If, however, they refuse to change even when you explain that they are making you feel angry and frustrated you may have to either reduce contact for a while or learn to tolerate their limitations and try to concentrate on any positive aspects of your relationship. Being ill requires a great deal of compromise and patience, but do not let people walk all over you. It is quite rational to feel angry when you are very ill. When used in the right way, anger can help you stand up for yourself and take control of your situation.

4

Depression

Not suprisingly, many people with ME are reluctant to admit that they ever even get depressed. Despite the growth in awareness about the disease, ME is still misdiagnosed by some doctors as a psychiatric condition and sufferers still have their symptoms dismissed as simply the result of inactivity and sick role behaviour. It is not that sufferers mind being told that they may be depressed on top of their ME, it is that they fear this label will be used to explain *all* their symptoms. It is natural that people want their illness to be properly recognised.

The problem with the term 'depression' is that it is over-used to describe almost any emotional state outside complete happiness and in doing so, its meaning has become muddied. Doctors and psychiatrists tend to define depression clinically by the presence of certain 'symptoms'. As a rule of thumb, they look to see if a patient displays at least three or four of the following to make a diagnosis:

- loss of energy
- sleep disturbance
- loss of weight
- loss of appetite
- inability to experience pleasure.

A more detailed list might include:

- insomnia and waking up in the early hours
- irritability and restlessness
- feelings of despair and hopelessness
- feelings of low self-esteem and guilt
- apathy and loss of interest in doing things previously enjoyed – especially sex
- thoughts of suicide or death
- diminished concentration or ability to think.

Looking down this list, it is not difficult to see how someone with ME who complains of having no energy, of having difficulties concentrating and of not being able to sleep properly, risks being told that they are clinically depressed. And even with a diagnosis of ME, the very presence of these 'symptoms' is often enough to persuade some that the disease is a largely depressive disorder. But look again at the list. Many of these 'symptoms' are present in a variety of physical diseases both as part of the disease and as a consequence of having it. Certainly, someone with ME will experience difficulties in their ability to think as cognitive dysfunction is a primary symptom of the disease. You are also, at some stage in your illness, likely to feel irritable and lacking in self-esteem simply from the strain of coping.

Experiencing emotions that are present in clinical depression such as low self-esteem and despair does not necessarily mean that you are clinically depressed. Certain situations demand certain responses. Anxiety, for example, may be an appropriate response to a genuinely worrying situation; fear, a realistic reaction to uncertainty and pain. Feeling worthless may be a quite rational response to living in a society that often deems those who are unable to work or look after themselves as of little value. This attitude often reveals itself in language, for example, the word used to describe an ill person: in-valid.

This chapter looks at the emotions that many sufferers experience as a natural response to living with a severe chronic illness. It applies to those who feel emotional pain; pain which is often described as 'depression'. We live in a culture that feels uncomfortable with expressions of great sadness and loss. People are wary of such strong emotions and shy away from them for fear that they may, somehow, be contaminated. Instead, psychic pain is safely lumped together and packaged as an illness in its own right, something that requires a specific label and particular treatment; in most cases, drugs. By defining your feelings as a particular condition, it is easier for others to separate your pain from 'normal', everyday experience. Your suffering is not seen as part of the human condition, a natural expression of grief over severe trials that could happen to anyone. Rather it is regarded as a manifestation of mental illness, a condition most people feel has absolutely nothing to do with their lives and, as such, can be more comfortably pushed away as something for doctors to deal with.

The problem of confusing ME with clinical depression arises when your doctor is more interested in ticking off lists than listening to what you are actually telling him. Symptoms that may at first sound similar, show themselves as quite distinct if given proper attention. For example, the loss of energy seen in ME patients is far more severe than that seen in depressed patients and marked by rapid muscle fatigue, a symptom not associated with clinical depression. Sleep disturbance can occur in ME but is usually intermittent throughout the night and not characterised by early morning wakening. Far from feeling apathetic, people with ME often display an advanced state of motivation frequently to the extent that they will push themselves to achieve something even though it makes them physically worse. Unlike the clinically depressed, ME sufferers, despite being unable to participate in many of the activities in life that give pleasure, can still find enjoyment in the smallest of things and possibly more so than before they became ill. These are just a few of the ways ME can be differentiated from depressive illness.

In this book the term 'depression' is used to define the gamut of emotions so often experienced by sufferers; emotions that can range from mild feelings of discontent to extreme feelings of despair and even thoughts of suicide. This use of the term 'depression' is defined against the term 'clinical depression' as described earlier.

In as much as it can be defined, 'clinical depression' denotes a severity and intractability that cannot be shifted by sympathy and understanding. It is unlikely to respond to self-help measures alone and necessitates professional help. If you are suffering from symptoms more usually associated with clinical depression such as feeling apathetic, losing interest in everything and everyone around you, feeling shut off as if there is a misted sheet of glass between you and others, feeling dead and empty inside, thinking frequently about suicide and being unable to be cheered up at all, then you should definitely tell your doctor and get professional help.

Depression in ME

Living with chronic illness saps your energy. Not only do you have to cope with physical symptoms that weigh you down, you also have the effects of the illness to cope with; the isolation, boredom, anxiety about the future and so on. There are many valid reasons for ill people to feel extremely unhappy – it would be rather odd if one felt *happy* about having one's life turned upside down by disease. For those with ME, the stigma and misunderstanding surrounding the illness accentuates the problems they already face and make coping that much more difficult. On top of this, there is now evidence to suggest that mood-swings (or what doctors call 'emotional lability') are an actual part of the disease process.

So how can you tell if your depressive feelings are part of ME – a symptom like any other – or simply a reaction to the stresses of living with it? Many sufferers report that they feel most depressed when their other symptoms are particularly bad. This could indicate that the fluctuation of their moods are directly linked to and an intrinsic part of the physical ups and downs of ME. At the same time, when you feel physically worse everything becomes more difficult to cope with and you inevitably feel more hopeless and depressed about your life. Even with minor ailments – such as the common cold – feeling miserable is a natural, biological reaction to feeling physically unwell. With a more serious disease this response is compounded by the grave consequences of long-term illness. The more ill you are, the harder your life is likely to be and the more genuinely depressing it becomes. It is understandable to feel down if you can no longer work or get out of the house, or if you are having a particularly rough week. In the final analysis, it does not really matter where your depression comes from. It is just as likely to be a mixture of both organic depression (coming from the disease itself) and reactive depression (a response to the immense strain of living with it).

But whether organic or reactive, your emotions are likely to be the same; feeling anxious, lonely, frightened, feeling that you are of little value as a person, that life no longer holds any meaning, feeling that things will never improve, that there is no point in struggling on. You may experience all or only some of these feelings and there may be other equally painful emotions. Sometimes they may slip into your life in a relatively mild form, dragging you down to a general feeling of disgruntlement and irritation. At other times they may come crashing into your life, drowning you under great black waves of despair for hours, weeks or even months at a time. One day you may be feeling all right and the next you can be tearing out your hair at the hopelessness and futility of life. Then all of a sudden, as swiftly as it appeared, the heavy cloud lifts and you feel 'normal' again.

Being unable to tell for certain why you get depressed, whether it is just another symptom of ME or the inevitable wax and wane of coping makes it doubly difficult to manage. Even worse is not knowing if or when the next bout will arrive or, when it does, if it will ever go away.

Anxiety

Anxiety, like mood-swings, may be another symptom of the disease. It often presents itself in a non-specific way, attributable to nothing in particular. Yet there may also be other explanations for sufferers' anxiety. Many seriously ill people experience anxiety about their health. Those with ME have a particular reason to feel anxious, because of the uncertainty surrounding diagnosis. As there is yet no diagnostic test for ME, sufferers have to rely on a clinical judgement that is often based on very little knowledge of the disease. Even the experts do not yet know all there is to know about ME. Having to rely on your doctor's judgement, in which you may not have a great deal of faith, can lead to many anxieties. One of the most common is that your doctor has failed to rule out other conditions. For all you know, you may have a life-threatening disease that produces the same symptoms as ME. Or you may have an illness that is treatable.

An alternative worry may be that your doctor, in dismissing any new symptom you may have as just another manifestation of ME, will miss the possibility that you might have another disease on top of the one you already have. As one sufferer put it:

'Just because you have one illness doesn't mean that you can't develop another'.

When you are continually ill it is natural that you become more conscious of what is happening to your body. After all, you have to listen to it carefully in order to manage your illness. Out of necessity you become highly attuned to what your body is telling you and this extra sensitivity, when coupled with feeling that you are not in control of your life or that you do not have enough information about the disease, can develop into anxiety. Just as someone who is nervous about flying focuses all their concentration on every detail of the flight and is hyper-conscious of every unusual sound or bit of turbulence, the person who is worried about their health is more aware than usual of any signs of change in their body.

One sufferer described how he would:

> examine every mole on my body convinced that I was now getting skin cancer. Then I'd notice that I was developing more severe headaches than usual and I'd worry about that. I wanted to tell my doctor but I was anxious that I'd either be told that I did have something else wrong with me or that I would be dismissed as a hypochondriac. In fact, I was anxious that I *was* becoming a hypochondriac. And anyway, even if I had been able to tell my doctor and he had been really understanding, I don't think I would have been very reassured because I'd tell myself, well what does he know, how can he be sure? After all it took him long enough to recognise that I had ME in the first place.

This vigilance over every perceived change in your body stems from a need to feel more in control of what is happening to you. Illness takes control away from you, it dictates how you feel, what you can and cannot do. By maintaining your anxiety about new symptoms you are, like the nervous air passenger, trying to convince yourself that you can direct events. By being constantly alert to your body you hope to be able to spot any sign of new disease and therefore feel more in control of your life. Unfortunately the opposite occurs because the more you observe your body, the more you notice to feel anxious about and the more impotent and less in charge you feel.

The anxiety that, as well as ME, there may be some other sinister disease ready to make life even more difficult, arises from a real concern that if one bad thing can happen to you so can another. When fate deals you a blow you do not necessarily feel strengthened by the experience. Rather than thinking, 'now that I've had to deal with this I can deal with anything', you are more likely to feel apprehensive about what else life has in store for you. Having been a victim of misfortune once you no longer have the confidence that bad things only happen to other people.

Feeling that you are not in command of your life can, in a similar way as discussed earlier with anger, lead to behaviour that borders on the obsessive. This behaviour often develops surreptitiously and stems from a deep-seated anxiety that if anything else were to happen you would be unable to cope in your weakened and vulnerable state.

One long-term and severely affected man was gripped by a fear that if something awful happened he would be unable to protect his wife and children. He developed his own response to try to deal with this fear:

'I find that I have to constantly check things around the house to make sure, for example, that the gas hob is switched off or the front door is properly locked. I try not to do this too often but checking just once doesn't reassure me so I have to check a few times. I can't seem to help it. I am plagued with the fear that if I don't check these things then something terrible will happen. Unfortunately, I do on occasions forget to switch off the gas or lock the front door. I've even left the key in the lock outside a number of times. I admit that I needn't do it so many times yet I feel there is some reason for my checking. In a way, it's my contribution to the protection of my family. I know that in the event of an accident or break-in I wouldn't be much use, I wouldn't be strong enough to fight off any robbers. My checking makes me feel more in control of my environment, that I'm minimising the risk of these things happening.'

There are many things to feel anxious about when you are long-term ill not least the more practical worries such as the possibility of losing your job, the difficulty of managing on welfare benefits and the anxiety that something might happen to the person who looks after you. On top of this you have to cope with the capriciousness of the disease; the fluctuating symptoms, the worries about getting worse, the anxiety about when or if you will get better. All these add to the anxiety that you may already be experiencing as a symptom of the disease itself.

Thinking about Death

ME provides you with plenty of time to think. As it takes away your energy it takes away your ability to keep busy. Spending many hours having to rest allows you time for contemplation you may never have previously had. You may become aware of time moving on while you seem to be standing still. Seeing others get on with their lives makes you notice all the more keenly how swiftly life is passing you by. You become aware of the finiteness of life and with this you come to appreciate your own mortality. When you were fit and active you may never have given death a second thought. It may have seemed distant and almost irrelevant in your vitality and strength.

People sometimes wonder why you should think about death if you are chronically ill – after all, your disease is not terminal. Yet when you are ill for a long time with a condition that saps your energy, especially if it does so severely, you find yourself in a limbo between life and death. Although the disease does not cause you to die, neither does it allow you to live fully. You exist somewhere between a full and complete life and a full and complete death, hence the common description of ME as 'the living death'.

Developing an increased awareness that one day you will die can motivate you to get the most out of your life despite your limitations. It can also drive you into a panicky terror that the months and, possibly, years are shooting past and you are left behind stuck in a permanent state of rest and inactivity, unable to make anything of your life. You may be tormented by the fear that if you do not recover you will grow old with nothing to look back on but the desert of your life. The possibility of facing death – even death at some unknown future date – after a life of lost hopes, emptiness and disappointment can be terrifying.

Isolation

Having ME can be a very lonely business. Many sufferers find that their illness puts a gulf between themselves and their family and friends. If you feel so ill that just getting through the day uses up all your energy, it can be difficult to continue to find much in common with, let alone see, your friends. Your lives are now so different and the growing chasm between you can feel almost impossible to bridge. If you are no longer able to work or take reponsibility for bringing up your children you lose what is the main focus of most people's lives. It can be difficult to think of anything to talk about when you are occupied with coping with illness while your friends are leading a normal existence. If you can no longer go out and socialise you lose touch with people. You may no longer be able to chat about mutual friends or the latest party or discuss the new film at the local cinema. You do still have things to say but, perhaps, about more passive interests such as what you have seen on TV or read in a book, about your thoughts and so on.

You may have sensitive friends who want to continue a relationship even if it has to change, but many may find the lack of mutual interests as well as the awkwardness they feel about ME enough reason to stop calling. It is probably not a conscious decision to cut you out of their life it is just that it feels more comfortable, less problematic, to see someone else instead.

Under normal circumstances, if you lose friends there are always opportunities to make new ones; at work, at the pub, at an evening class etc. But if you are unable to work or get out of the house regularly, or even if you can work but have to spend all your energies doing so, it can be very difficult indeed to meet anyone new. Even if you have the energy to go out there is still the stigma of ME to overcome. One woman, in desperation to make some friends, put an advert in the local paper:

> I got a good response and arranged to meet a few people. It was a bit awkward but everything was okay until the inevitable came up; the question about what I did. I said that I wasn't able to work because I had ME and everything completely changed. I ended up having to explain all about ME and how it wasn't just a case of feeling a bit tired. I felt I had to justify why I wasn't working and prove that I was really ill. It made the whole meeting exhausting and strained. I met a couple of other people who were okay about ME but I soon lost contact with them as I kept having to cancel our meetings when I felt unwell. I did explain that sometimes I wouldn't be able to get out but I don't think they could be bothered with the extra hassle.

Sometimes the only way of keeping friendships is to pretend – if you are able – that there is nothing really wrong with you. It may or may not be known that you have ME, but there is an unspoken agreement that it is never mentioned and that talking about your life with illness is completely out of bounds. This may help you maintain some sort of social life but putting on a 'good front' has its price. It can be painfully lonely to feel that you are only acceptable to others so long as you hide who you are. And knowing that everyone else is returning to normal, healthy lives while you crash out in bed to recover from the exertion of socialising for an hour or so adds to your feeling of isolation, of being different in a way that nobody seems to understand.

If you are housebound it can feel almost impossible to meet anyone at all. There may be a support group in your area but being unable to get out you are not able to attend. There may be a telephone 'listening ear' service but you may be looking for a chat – preferably face to face – not counselling. There are still ways that the severely affected can find company (see Chapter Eight) but it can be very hard to accept that you may not be able to develop a good circle of friends to replace those friendships you have lost.

When you find yourself in a difficult situation you begin to find out who your friends are. Sadly, many relationships do not stand up to the test. Being chronically ill, you may need a little more support and understanding than usual, but it is unusual to find people who are prepared to make the extra effort, particularly if it looks as if you are going to be ill for a long time. Many long-term sufferers find that they do have friends who stand by them during the first few years but when they fail to recover even these friendships start to fall away. This can be especially hard because the longer you are ill the more you need your friends. It takes a particularly thoughtful and caring person to be a good friend through bad times that can last for years. Unfortunately, not enough people are willing to make the changes – however small – necessary to incorporate an ill person into their social life.

Perhaps the most profoundly isolating aspect of ME is that you no longer fit into a particular role. It can be immensely difficult to find a definition for yourself with which you feel comfortable. Although you may be severely disabled by ME, you may not feel altogether happy using the term 'disabled' because your disabilities are 'invisible' and your condition misunderstood. Even though disability affects all kinds of people with all kinds of conditions, most people understand it in terms of loss of limbs or the use of a stick or a wheelchair. There are sufferers who use such physical aids but for the majority who do not, this definition of disability does not seem to quite fit the fluctuating 'flat battery' condition of ME.

At the same time, although ME *is* a serious disease, you may not feel justified in describing it as such because people often only consider an illness to be serious if it is potentially life-threatening. 'Serious' illnesses are those like cancer or multiple sclerosis even if they can often allow sufferers to lead a more active life than many people with ME. Describing your illness as 'chronic' fails to convey the potential severity of ME. Most people understand 'chronic illness' to be a less serious condition, one that allows those affected to lead relatively normal lives. Few people realise that it can have just as devastating effect on your life as other, so-called 'more-serious' diseases.

On top of the difficulty of self-definition, is the stigma of ME. When you know that many people still see the disease as 'yuppie flu', as being just a bit tired, or worse, as an excuse for malingering, you can begin to dread even having to admit that you have the illness at all. When others' ignorance can make you feel like an outcast it can be tempting to avoid social interaction altogether.

Despair

The strain of having to cope with great change in your life, with disbelief and rejection, with isolation and loss while at the same time feeling constantly ill can nudge the strongest person into despair. Despair does not only come to people who are ill. It can happen to anyone in crisis; from a person who is in serious debt, to someone who has lost a loved one through death or divorce. But the kind of grief experienced by someone who is long-term and seriously ill is quite different from the grief from these kinds of losses. In normal bereavement, the event that causes the grief gradually recedes. With this movement, the grieving person can travel further and further away from the source of their pain hence the adage, 'time heals'. People in this situation do sometimes get stuck in their grief but as time passes, and with support and understanding, there is the potential to pick up the pieces and start again.

With chronic illness, however, the source of your grief – being ill – is constantly with you. Your inability to work, your isolation, your dependence on others are not due to circumstances from which you can move away and begin to build a life again. Chronic illness is an ongoing process. Unless you get better your feelings of loss – although able to be tempered – will remain with you to a certain degree until you recover. The possibility of starting your life afresh can only come when you are well enough to rebuild it.

Although many sufferers do eventually get the opportunity to start again as they get better some do not and these people have to face, with the continuation of their illness, a life of prolonged loss. There *are* ways of making tolerable a life with long-term ME; by changing your reaction to it, by improving your coping skills and so on. But for many the struggle to keep going in the face of no change or improvement can hardly seem worth the effort.

Thinking about Suicide

Tragically, the pain and loneliness of living with ME becomes for some people too much to bear. The world seems an irretrievably hostile place and life within it pointless. To the severely ill and long-term affected in particular, the endlessness of feeling ill all the time, the isolation, frustration, and agony of loss, together with the dimming of hopes for recovery lead to thoughts of escape. There seems to be no possibility of ever being able to lead a tolerable life with ME and only one way out; suicide.

You do not have to be clinically depressed to think about suicide. Many people who are very ill fantasise about suicide at some point in their life as a last resort strategy if everything becomes too unbearable. This does not mean that they are necessarily going to carry out their fantasy. Feeling that if things get intolerable you do have some vestige of control over your life, some way of escape, is enough of a release for many people. But for others, particularly those with little love or support around them, these fantasies can turn into reality.

Perhaps if sufferers were allowed to give voice to some of their despair and people were more prepared to hear their pain, suicides would be less common. There is an unending pressure not to feel 'sorry for yourself'; from media stories of plucky invalids who never 'give in' or allow their 'spirit to be broken', to family and friends who, when you try to talk about how hard life is, silence you by saying, 'try not to think about it, it'll only depress you'. Expressing how you really feel challenges the myth of the spirited martyr who fights to the bitter end. In reality, there is little division between those who fight their disease and those who do not. Most ill and disabled people want to get better and do everything they can, within their limits, to achieve this. The people on television who perpetuate the, 'I'm a fighter' image may have difficult times ahead but are usually still leading fairly normal lives. Disablement through disease is a great leveller and when their lives begin to be profoundly affected by their condition, they act like most people who are seriously ill; burdened and often depressed by their situation.

Your inability to always put on a good face, your need to display feelings of desperation may be too threatening to those close to you. They are likely to find it too painful, too disturbing to hear that you do not want to live. Yet if this is how you feel, you must express it. Ill people need to be allowed to face the worst, to talk about anxieties about the future. You need to talk of your fear of not getting any better or even deteriorating. This is not being negative or pessimistic. On the contrary, it is a positive and brave step towards learning how to look forward and prepare yourself for what may come your way. Being listened to, being taken seriously without judgement, without being told that you should not look too far ahead or dwell on painful feelings or that you do not really mean it when you say that sometimes you just want to die, can often be enough to keep these expressions of despair from progressing into action.

Dealing with Depression

If you are thinking about suicide – even if you do not think that you would actually carry it out – do tell someone. However painful or difficult it is to speak about how you feel, do not keep it to yourself. Even if you believe that you are in control of your suicidal thoughts, that they act as a safety valve to help you cope and, therefore, nobody else needs to know about them, it is still a good idea to share how you feel, because sometimes you do not have as much control as you think. There may come a time, perhaps when you are going through a particularly bad spell of health, or having to cope with an unforseen crisis, when your thoughts about suicide can turn from being a preventative fantasy to being an improvised plan of action. Without even being aware of it, you may be getting increasingly depressed and before you can do anything to stop it, find yourself in a labyrinth of despair from which suicide seems the only escape. Some sufferers may feel wary of telling their doctor about suicidal thoughts for fear that the very real physical symptoms of ME will be undermined. When you are feeling suicidal the last thing you need is to have your physical illness dismissed and the real misery of your predicament ignored. If you fear that this will be the response from your doctor, go and see someone else in your practice. Explain that you are chronically ill and that the strain of coping is making you feel depressed. Do not feel pressured into explaining about ME if you do not wish to. You are entitled to help, such as counselling or anti-depressant treatment for your emotional problems whether or not you have a physical disease. If you really cannot face seeing a doctor then at least tell a relative or friend about how desperate you feel so there is someone who knows how bad the situation is and can arrange, on your behalf, the extra help you need.

If you remain ill for years without improvement it can seem as if there is no chance that things will ever get better. It is easy in this situation to lose all hope. But one thing you can hold on to is that even if your health does not improve, your coping skills in all likelihood will. This in itself will make you feel better about life. It is absolutely vital that you get as much support as you can to help you manage. It can be hard to ask for help but if that is what it takes to survive then you have to do it. Your doctor can refer you to a counsellor (who may be able to do home visits if you cannot get out) who will be able to listen to your grief and desolation. There are also, as mentioned earlier, anti-depressants that (with careful handling of dosage) may well be of help.

Over time, your stamina for emotional pain will strengthen and things you previously found so hard will be easier to bear. You will, inevitably, have to learn to manage a certain amount of pain on your own. But you do not always have to suffer alone. There are people out there who are willing to help. You can pick up the phone and call the ME 'listening ear' service and talk to someone who really understands what living with the illness is like, or you can telephone your local Samaritans. Sometimes when you feel very low you can believe that nobody wants to hear from you. You may feel that you are burdening others by telling them your problems. But these services have been especially set up for you and others in your situation. You do not have to be afraid of being an encumbrance on the people who run these helplines. They would not have volunteered to listen if they did not want to know or hear about your troubles. It may not seem very personal talking to strangers but it can often be liberating to discuss your life with someone who is not involved yet who does care enough to hear your pain and want you to carry on.

The therapy of talking to someone who understands may not have the power to change the fact that you are ill, but it can help you come to terms with it. Being free to talk as often as you need helps to empty the bottle of despair until it fills up and needs emptying again. When you have shared some of the torment you feel, your despair will loosen its grip a little and thoughts of suicide should diminish. Life will, once again, feel that bit more manageable.

Even if you never think of suicide but still feel depressed at times, it is important to express how you feel. Often, it is only when you let out your pain that you find some inner peace. You can use any of the methods discussed in this and the previous chapter to help release and cope with your anguish. In addition, there are other things that may help.

If you sometimes feel overrun with anxiety, try to see if there is anything in particular (apart from being ill!) that is making you feel this way and if you can do something about it. Small and niggling worries can build up into one massive anxiety. By taking a systematic and organised approach to the management of your illness you can often take care of smaller anxieties before they get out of hand. Do not, for example, struggle on with the housework, deal with bills, get the shopping in etc. if you are not really well enough. You will only end up worrying that the house is a mess, that you are late with your payments or that you have not enough food in the house. Even if you do not like the idea of having to rely on others, you have to face up to the fact that you cannot manage on your own and that you need help. Get all the practical assistance you can. Tell your doctor that you are finding it difficult to physically cope and get a home help. Contact Social Services and make sure you tell them exactly how difficult your life is. You may be entitled to all sorts of services ranging from meals on wheels and help with transport to domiciliary library services and disability aids.

If your anxiety is manifesting itself in obsessive behaviour such as an urge to touch a switch several times for 'good luck' or constant checking, allow yourself a small number of touches or checks, but try to reduce the number slowly so that it does not escalate out of control. If it is already out of control and is taking over your life then you must seek medical help. The last thing you need as well as ME is a full-blown obsessive compulsive disorder.

Although popular wisdom has it that the best way to deal with fears is simply not to think about them, the truth is in fact, quite the opposite. The only way to cope with any fear is to bring it out into the open and face up to it. Again, it helps to talk to a counsellor or some other good listener who can stay with you and support you while you explore what really frightens you. Fear is often a way of trying to stay in control of a situation, but it almost always ends up controlling you. If you can look fear in the face and embrace your terrors you will find that their hold on you eventually weakens.

If you have bouts of feeling convinced that because you have been unlucky once misfortune is bound to strike again, try to put your situation into context. It is easy to catastrophise life when you are unwell and feeling vulnerable because the world does seem a more hostile and frightening place and if something else did happen it would genuinely be more diffi-cult – being ill – for you to cope. But take a look around you. How many people do you know (ME friends apart!) who have been victim to significant misfortune? Most people have prob-lems, but shattering, life-altering tragedies are not *that* common. There is no reason to believe that just because you have been unlucky once you should be singled out again. Bad luck strikes indiscriminately and does not have it in for you personally.

If you know that you suffer from mood swings and spells of depression it is a good idea to plan in advance things that might help you cope. Put aside a pile of books you particularly want to read, or if you are unable to read much, some maga-zines or books with interesting pictures and photographs. Plan small treats for yourself and save them up; some special oils for a long soak in the bath, something a bit unusual to eat (if a sensitised stomach doesn't forbid it) such as a special packet of biscuits or something you have not tasted before. If you can afford it, buy yourself something; a record or CD, a book, a video, a new pair of slippers. There are plenty of mail-order catalogues around if you cannot get out of the house. It may not amount to much but it is still important to have even small things to look forward to and raise the spirits when you feel especially down. Often when you are feeling depressed you can shift your mood a little simply by occupying your mind in this way with something unrelated to your illness. If you feel you could manage, think about getting a pet. They make excellent and undemanding companions. There are organisations that find and train dogs especially for disabled people (See Appendix:'Useful Addresses').

At times when you have been particularly depressed you will, no doubt, have been told by a well-meaning relative or friend to think about people worse off than yourself – the starving millions'. It is a way of telling you that what you have to put up with is not as bad as it could be and therefore you have nothing really to complain about.

Being told to put your life into perspective by people who are perfectly well and living active and normal lives is not only a cheek but also serves to make you feel guilty for ever feeling bad about your situation. Yet you should not throw away the idea altogether. You may not feel that you have much to be thankful for but often, just thinking about how much worse things could be can make a difficult life seem just that bit more attractive. Comparing your life to people in a worse situation, however, has to come from you and you alone. Only then can seeing your suffering in relation to others be helpful. Knowing that you are not the only one to have been singled out to have a rough time, that there are many people in this world – even if they are not right on your doorstep – who lead arduous and painful lives over which they have little control can help you feel less alone. Knowing what you have lost is painful but recognising that what you have left may still be more than others can give you strength to continue.

Even though those around you may be very lucky, their lives tarnished with relatively minor and manageable problems, the vast majority of people in this world are not so fortunate. Seeing your life with ME within a broader frame of reference can enable you to see that, even though it may not immediately feel this way, your life is not so very different from most people living on this planet. What has happened is that you have now left the privileged minority and joined, instead, the majority for whom life is a daily struggle and good fortune something that can never be taken for granted. You may not be starving but you are nevertheless still engaged in a struggle for survival.

Do not feel a failure for being depressed. You cannot help the way you feel and these emotions are a natural part of the grieving process. Instead of chastising yourself for feeling down, acknowledge how much you have to cope with and congratulate yourself for the stamina and tenacity you have developed to be able to carry on.

5

Acceptance

If someone had asked you when you first became ill if you could ever get used to it your answer would probably have been a resounding 'No!' If you had thought about it, the idea of accepting the disease as a constant in your life may have seemed not only horrifying but also defeatist. Instructed by your doctor to 'fight' it, urged on by your family not to 'give in', encouraged by friends telling stories of other sufferers recovering through their own efforts, you take it for granted that with the right attitude you can and will beat this illness.

But as time passes and despite your best endeavours you do not beat the illness, the idea that you can wage war to bring about your recovery starts to feel rather hollow. Slowly, you realise that however hard you fight ME it seems to have a mind of its own and that other than managing it as best you can, you do not have as much control over it as you first thought. This realisation is painful. Standing up to your illness felt brave, it gave you a feeling that you were in control, that you could succeed over it and 'win' the reward of a return to 'normal' life. By going into battle against ME you could hold back many of the feelings of anger and despair that accompany any real acknowledgment of what havoc this disease has caused in your life. Also, because you were surrounded by people egging you on to try more and more therapies and rewarding you for keeping up the good fight, you were encouraged to continue denying the reality of your situation. The pain and fear of even admitting the possibility that your present level of health might be with you for a long time or even, God forbid, that it might continue for ever, kept you going in your struggle against the disease.

When you finally let go of this struggle and start facing the very frightening prospect that ME may be around for longer than you may be able to bear, you are then in a position to begin to accept your life as it is, without having to see it only in the context of getting better. You begin to understand that constantly feuding against your body, against what you are now, will get you nowhere. Whether you like it or not, you are stuck – for the time being at least – with this illness. Denying this essential fact because you can only see your existence as viable if you are constantly chasing a cure, denies you the potential to make something of your life even with illness.

Accepting ME as part of your life does not mean that you accept the role of passive victim or that you want to be ill. Rather, it means that you are brave enough to open your eyes to the real situation and accept the hand that fate has played in it. Above all, it means that you have made the decision that you are going to make a life with your illness rather than against it.

Of course, this is not always easy. You would think that being ill for a long time would inure you to its more painful aspects. Instead, you still seem to grieve for what you have lost, you still seem to get angry and frustrated over the same things. You begin to wonder if you will ever get to that point of acceptance where you will finally feel at peace with your life.

But, in truth, no such point really exists. Your feelings of denial, anger and depression will remain with you to some degree until the day you recover and even past that point if you have been unable to resolve past hurts. What will happen instead is that if you are able to express these feelings they will, over time, diminish in frequency and intensity and become easier to deal with.

Acceptance within the context of ME is not about coming to the end of the grieving process and then feeling completely happy and content. Rather, it means that your grief, though still painful, will no longer dominate your life as it once did. You will learn to accept your feelings as a natural part of coping with chronic ill health and just as you gain an understanding and tolerance of your physical symptoms, you will also develop a certain toughness, a resilience to the emotional highs and lows that go with them. Acceptance means acknowledging the pain of all you have lost and all you have now to cope with. It means no longer living in the past or for the future, but coming to terms with the life you have now and deciding to live that life as best you can.

Hope

Everyone needs hope when they are ill; hope that you will get better; hope that even if you do not you will be able to cope more easily; hope that your family will be supportive, your friends understanding; hope that, perhaps, next week you will be able to go out. Hope gets you through the day – perhaps tomorrow will be better – it encourages you to carry on week in, week out and, if necessary, year after year. It holds up a pinpoint of light to follow through the dark tunnel of illness and despair.

But there is also another side to hope. There is false hope, frustrated hope, hope that keeps you in a prison of anticipation and prevents you from getting on with your life and making the most of what you have here and now.

Living with ME can be so difficult that you may not be able to contemplate making a life with it. Instead you focus all your energy on getting better. You manufacture deadlines for yourself; by next week I shall be well enough to get out of bed, this time next year I will be fit enough to return to work, in a couple of years I shall be completely well again. Having some faith that your health will improve, even if that improvement is small, can keep you going. But if your hopes for the future become concrete expectations you set yourself up for disappointment. If you focus on a particular date when you are going to recover, when life will be all right again, how are you going to feel if, as so often happens, that time comes and you are still ill? Looking forward to being well again may have got you through the months, but the disappointment of a hope frustrated can be crushing. You may say to yourself, 'Okay, it didn't happen this year, maybe next year I shall be luckier'. But how long can you keep shifting forward the deadline for recovery?

Many people with ME, particularly those in the first year or so of the illness, do get better and, of course, you may completely recover too. But what happens in the meantime? What happens if you are unlucky and you do not get better, or are ill for several years? Can you afford to spend the rest of your life waiting for something that may take a long time to happen or may not even happen at all? Just because your life is no longer as it used to be, can it no longer offer you anything until and unless you are well?

By focusing completely on recovery, on life as you hope it to be, you dismiss the life that you already have. By concentrating all your efforts on getting better, on returning to what your life used to be like before ME you risk falling apart if these hopes are dashed. If, on the other hand, you try to see what you can salvage from the wreckage of your illness you have a real chance of making something of your life; something which is not dependent on a recovery that may or may not occur. Instead of putting your life on hold, you can say to yourself, 'Of course I want more than anything to get better but I have to be patient. Even if things are not exactly how I wish them to be, and even though I am limited in what I can do, I am still going to live the bit of life that I have left to the fullest.'

By shifting your aim away from 'getting well again' and instead towards working with what you already have, the heat is taken out of having to recover. You can get off the tortuous treadmill of hope and despair and feel that even if the worst happens and you do not get better you can still make something of your life. Others may not view what you have as amounting to very much and may believe that your only chance of a life worth living is to get better. They may pressurise you not to 'give up' or 'give in'. But you have the right, regardless of what anyone else thinks, to live your life as it is now without being held ransom to the future.

It is in your interest to make as much as you can out of your present existence, to imbue it with something that will give it meaning. No longer allowing your whole life to centre around getting better does not mean that you have lost hope of regaining your health, and it certainly does not mean that you are happy to remain ill. What it does mean is that you are not prepared to base your life on a double-edged hope full of let downs and disillusionment, but on a more realistic hope that concentrates on making the most of your present health while still holding on to the possibility that you may, if not get completely well, get a little better and if not even that then, at least, get better at coping.

Positivity

There can be enormous pressure from other people to put on a front of cheerful acceptance, particularly if you have been unwell for many years. There is the expectation that by now 'you should have got used to it' and any expression of pain or loss is viewed as evidence that you are wallowing in self-pity or negativity and that, maybe, you do not really want to get better. It can be easy to beat yourself up about not being positive enough, about not always being hopeful and certain that you are going to get better, for feeling depressed and disenchanted about how your life has turned out.

But real positivity is not about pretending that everything is fine and that you are quite happy with having such a reduced life. Real positivity is not a performance to placate others. It does not consist of denying how awful things are, or appearing happy all the time, or constantly making light of your disabilities. Real positivity is accepting the limitations your illness makes on you and yet still being able to appreciate the little that you have left. It is like having half a glass of your favourite drink and rather than regretting that it is half empty, being glad that it is at least half full. If you are constantly harking back to what you used to have, then your present existence will be intolerable. Life will only seem worthwhile if you can find something in it – however small – that you can value and feel good about.

It may take a long time to get to this point. During the initial storm of becoming ill when your life comes tumbling down and you are walking through the ruins, numb from shock, trying to get used to what has happened, you are unlikely to be ready to start picking up the remnants and seeing what you can manage to rebuild. You cannot do this until you have dealt with denial and expressed your anger and despair. Only then, when you have experienced a large part of your grief will life appear less turbulent and leave you feeling strong enough to take a long look at what options are left open to you and what you can make out of the remnants that are left. There will be many times when the pain of your bereavement is so overwhelming that the last thing you feel like being is constructive or positive. You may feel that the effort of trying to scrape together some sort of life with ME is simply not worth the emotional energy. There is nothing wrong in feeling this way. You are bound to feel low, particularly if you are having a bad spell physically. Living with blackness and despair as well as optimism and hope is all part of coping with serious chronic illness. Being positive does not mean that you always have to feel good about your life – that would be impossible! You cannot force yourself to feel positive (although see Appendix for exercises that may help shift you into a less melancholic frame of mind). Positivity means accepting the ebb and flow of your moods while having made the decision that, however miserable you feel about your life in general, you are still going to try, when you feel emotionally up to it, to make the most of your life.

Being positive means being focused and organised. You have to be prepared to let go of wanting to achieve everything – or even anything – you may have once hoped to do. You have to assess how much energy you have and start to prioritise. Perhaps you will still be able to keep on some work if you can arrange to do it from home. Maybe you will feel up to having a trip out if you accept a lower level of tidiness in the house; talk for longer if you reduce the number of people you see; read more often if you lie in bed to do so rather than sit up. Your options do become more limited the iller you are but even if you are severely affected there are still choices to be made. You may not be strong enough to write letters, but perhaps you can keep up a correspondence by speaking your 'letter' onto a tape recorder, you may not be able to read for long but maybe you can listen to talking books instead and so on.

Making choices with ME is usually deciding between doing one thing or another. It can be very frustrating and hard to accept that you may not be able to do both. It may hardly seem worthwhile to take up an interest if you can only spend a tiny amount of time on it each day or week. Yet it is remarkable how progress can be made when you apply yourself consistently to one task even if it feels painfully slow at times; a few stitches a day eventually make a tapestry.

If you have very little energy it is vital to examine your daily routine and see if there are any savings to be made in it. You may not be immediately aware of them, but some activities could be draining you more than you think. Is there anyone in your life who, whenever you talk with them, leave you feeling particularly tense and exhausted? If so, perhaps there is a way of reducing the effect by limiting their visits or your conversations with them. Are you keeping to a routine which may no longer be suitable for your present state of health? You may be clinging to a sense of normality by forcing yourself to do things that you can barely manage. It is painful to let go; of how you like your house to be run; of taking your child to school; of going out to see friends; of going for a walk to the shops. But if pushing yourself to manage these things makes you ill you are going to have to make changes to your life.

For example, you may still be just about able to visit friends but if on your return you have to lie in bed to recover for several hours surely it is better to have friends visit you? Of course, this can be problematic because asking people to do something can change the dynamic of a relationship; it puts you in the position of being needy and people often feel uncomfortable about requests – however minor – being made of them. Some of your relationships will not be able to withstand any change so it is important to think very carefully about which of your friendships, if any, are flexible enough to cope with a slightly different social set-up. But if you can maintain some relationships without having to go out to socialise, you will obviously have more energy to devote to those that rely solely on your ability to go out and keep up a 'normal' appearance. If you continue to try and maintain this appearance with every one of your friends you stand a good chance of becoming so ill that you will be unable to see anyone, whether or not they come to visit you.

Likewise, you may have enough energy to go out but are unable to go to the places you want because you cannot walk far. You know a wheelchair or a stick with a stool might make you more mobile but you may feel reluctant to make your disability visible. Although there are many disadvantages to having an 'invisible' illness there is one advantage; being able to go out without having to declare to the world that you are any different from anyone else. Even though you know inside how restricted your life is, it can be a great release not to have to worry about what others think of you. Using a wheelchair may increase your mobility but it also exposes you to unwelcome attention. Unfortunately, people often feel it is acceptable to stare at wheelchair users and the stress of maybe having to face some ignorant comment can put you off using one altogether. This is particularly the case if you are using one in conjunction with a little walking, something that flies in the face of the stereotype of all wheelchair users being permanently bound to their chairs. Even though you know that wheelchairs and sticks are just aids to make your life easier, the reality is that using them can and often does make you more self-conscious. Going out when you have ME is enough of a balancing act without having to deal with any additional stress. The pros and cons of using a wheelchair (if you are up to it) have to be weighed carefully; getting about more easily and appearing disabled against limiting your mobility and fitting in with the crowd. The important thing is to recognise that, if you can handle the consequences, certain choices are available even when you are very ill with ME.

With a condition like ME it is essential to save energy whenever you can. If you feel ill after going to the doctor's surgery make sure you get a home visit. Whether or not you are able to make the journey is irrelevant; the point about this illness is that sufferers often can do something but suffer for it afterwards. You may find it difficult to ask your doctor to come round to see you when you know that, even if it is going to make you feel worse, you can actually make the journey but if you are so ill that, say, you can only get out of the house about once a week it is evidently easier for a healthy GP, however busy, to come and visit you than the other way around. S/he is also unlikely to understand exactly how ill you are if the only time s/he sees you is when you have got dressed and made the effort to get up and go out. With a home-visit your doctor gets the opportunity to see you as you really are.

Make sure you take advantage of any other domiciliary services that are available; arrange for your shopping to be delivered; send out your ironing; make sure people come to you rather than the other way around. Some sufferers have little choice about being completely reliant on others but you do not have to be completely bedbound or even housebound to ask others to do things for you. In fact, if you do still have a bit of energy it is vital that you make the best use of it by letting others take care of the more practical aspects of your daily life. You have not only to consider what you are able to do on a particular day, but what energy is left to spend on something enjoyable; something that gives some meaning to your life. For your emotional well-being you need to leave some energy for something other than just basic survival.

Power

Being seriously ill can be a profoundly disempowering experience. You may no longer be able to rely on the conventional props of life: work, social life, that used to give you self-esteem and a sense of who you are. Your position in society has now changed. Once you may have been an active and esteemed member of your profession, family or community. Now you may be regarded as of little consequence; someone whose opinions are no longer sought; a person no longer deserving of consideration or respect.

Now that you are unable to direct your life as you once did because your body tells you what you can or cannot do, people no longer seem to treat you as a capable and responsible adult who, despite physical limitations, is still able to be consulted and listened to. Instead you are infantilised, chivvied along, told what is good for you and commented upon as merely a perplexing problem to be solved. Doctors start to assign stigmatising labels to you. Family and friends feel able to 'explain' your illness in a way that imputes unfavourable things about your personality. When you were fit and well you were a free agent, you did not have to listen to others' misrepresentation of your character, you did not have to stand for being told what to do, ignored and belittled. Your life was your own and you were at its helm. With illness all this has changed. Now everyone seems to believe that they have a right – even a duty – to define, comment upon and govern your life. And the worst thing is that you have so little energy you can hardly manage to challenge them.

You may certainly feel this way during the first few months or even years of being ill. During this time your energies are occupied with learning about the disease, trying to come to terms with the fact that you are seriously ill and attempting to hold the pieces of your crumbling life together. You feel bombarded with things to cope with and have few enough resources as it is to even think about how to regain some of the personal power that has been taken away from you. But there does come a time when you begin to feel more settled. You feel less like a leaf being tossed in the wind of a storm, less susceptible to being pushed around and having your life directed for you. With less energy being spent worrying about why people undermine and dismiss ME, less energy spent raging against the unfairness of being ill, less energy despairing about what you have lost, that tiny part deep inside you that has kept you going starts to grow. And as it gets stronger you begin to feel more stable, your life more rooted and you start to develop a real sense of indignation that people can treat you so badly, so insensitively when you are at your most vulnerable. You realise with force that you do not, after all, have to put up with the denial, the interference, the ignorance of others. You begin to see that you have a right – however ill and dependent you are – to be treated with respect, to govern your own life as far as is physically possible and to be your own person. And you make the decision that from this time on you will not allow people to walk all over you.

Only when you are more accustomed to being ill, more hardened to the inevitable ups and downs in your life, will you be in a position to rebuild the confidence you may have lost during the initial phase of your illness. Only then can you see that however diminished your existence is, you still possess some power as well as the choice to exercise that power. Yes, there will still be situations over which you have no control; you still have to see a doctor for your sick notes, have medical examinations, have some contact with other people and all these relationships are open to abuse. But even within these, there is the opportunity to take increasing charge over how you are treated.

If someone is abusing their position of power, treating you differently because you are ill it is up to you – because nobody else is going to do it – to make it absolutely clear that this behaviour is unacceptable. People who tend to take advantage of vulnerable people, who do not think twice about saying undermining and impudent things are often the first to buckle under when you challenge them. It would be nice to think that you are met with courtesy and respect whoever you are and whatever position you hold in society but, sadly, in the real world the lower status you are, the worse you are generally treated. The poor status that the ill hold in our culture makes you more vulnerable to mistreatment. If you then also appear timid and unsure of yourself, you are even more likely to be abused. At the time when you most need others to be kind and sensitive you learn the hard lesson that people tend to treat you as you allow yourself to be treated. This does not mean that you are to blame for the discrimination and ignorance you face, but it does mean that, to a certain extent, you can encourage better behaviour from people when you insist, by the way you act as well as the things you say, that you will not be bossed around or humiliated.

Developing this sort of self-preservation and becoming assertive is not the easiest thing to do when you feel ill. It does not come naturally to most people but it is something you can, and have to, learn (see 'Useful Books' in Appendix). Your weariness of being victim to whatever piece of nonsense others feel like saying or never being allowed to make your own decisions and so on will motivate you to develop these skills. They include learning to say 'No' and sticking to it; learning how to refuse to listen to damaging comments; learning how to avoid people who make you feel worse. You need to stop submitting to patronising and offensive behaviour from anyone even if they are in a position of authority. You need to learn how to speak your mind rather than bottling it up and feeling depressed afterwards and, above all, you need to stop apologising for the way you are.

The more you actually put into practice the conviction that however disabled you are and whatever illness you happen to have, you are worthy of respect, the more you will find that people will give you that respect.

Re-building your life with ME

Coping with ME is likely to be the biggest challenge of your life. Of course, everyone has challenges to face; unemployment, bereavement, divorce etc., but none of these demand such a complete change to almost every aspect of one's existence. Such everyday trials certainly test a person, but living with ME – particularly long-term and severe ME – can push you to the limit of endurance. Because it can take away so much from you; your job, your friends, your family, your ability to look after yourself, to walk, to feel anything but continually ill, it can feel as if you are hardly living at all. Life is energy and ME robs you of that energy. Without this essence of life how can you live?

And while you have all this to come to terms with, you must face the biggest challenge of all; that however extreme the pain and loss, people often doubt that you are going through anything of any consequence at all. The little energy you have left is drained away by having to deal with the acute alienation and isolation of being disbelieved, undermined and stigmatised. Living with a disease that seeps into every crevice of your life and has the potential to carry on indefinitely is, as the Sufis say, like trying to cross a chasm of fire on a human hair.

You need tremendous courage to choose to carry on when your whole existence is challenged. Each day that you make that choice to continue is a decision of bravery because the journey can be so painful and lonely.

And the real test is not only to survive ME but to make some sort of life with it; to come to terms with whatever your present level of health has to offer you, to accept and sometimes even appreciate the ways in which you are different.

By acknowledging the tremendous difficulties you face each and every day; physical, emotional, social, economic, you can, perhaps, begin to recognise that you have a unique perspective on the world. Your experience of living with this illness gives you a particular insight into what it is to suffer, what it is to live differently from others.

Very few people take the time to really reflect on what life is about because thinking too deeply can be painful. Most people are so caught up with their jobs, their families and their social life they leave no room to savour the small things in life which might, in fact, give the most pleasure. You have been placed in a situation that leaves you with no choice but to think a lot, to contemplate your position in the world, to appreciate things that you may never previously have noticed. Although given a choice you would willingly give up the pain and loss of your life and opt for an easier existence, your experience of such pain intensifies your experience of pleasure and joy when it happens. So many people take what they have for granted. Look around you—how many happy faces you see. Even with all their good fortune people still complain about their lives, carry on living in ways that they could easily change, hanker after more and more and seem dissatisfied and quite oblivious to the blessings they have.

It may seem that having a unique perspective on life and appreciating the little things it has to offer is small compensation for the trials you have to put up with. Of course you would prefer to forgo these to return to your former life. And one day you may again have all that you once had. But in the meantime you have to accept that you are in this situation, that you are different from what you were and that you might as well recognise some of the things that illness brings to your life that you otherwise might never have experienced. Yes, living without so much of what is pleasurable in life can be unbearable at times and there is no getting away from that fact.

But there is one thing that long-term illness gives you that very few people ever attain. That is the opportunity to develop an internal strength and self-worth which is not dependent on having an impressive job or lots of money; a self-reliance that can cope with immense hardship without relying on fickle friendships; a sense of self with a sturdiness that cannot be broken down. These things, once you have them – and coping with an illness like ME does give you the potential to develop these strengths – can never be taken away from you. You may not have asked to be long-term ill, you may not have wanted to have to deal with pain and suffering, but doing so has made you a person who can endure and that has to be something to be proud of.

Section two

QUESTIONS &

ANSWERS

6

Medical Matters

My GP refuses to believe ME exists, never mind that I have it.
Should I try to convince him or look for another doctor?

If your doctor insists that a particular disease doesn't exist there isn't a great deal you can do to change his mind. You could try and educate him but if he's the kind of doctor who dismisses illnesses out of hand he is also likely to be the kind who dislikes patients knowing more than he does. Even though there is now scientific evidence that ME is an organic condition with potentially devastating effect, there remain many doctors who are ignorant about the disease.

Even when such evidence is produced, these doctors are unwilling to challenge their initial prejudice about the illness. It isn't easy to lose face and admit, even to yourself, that perhaps you were wrong so they prefer to cling to their original opinion until there is absolute, incontrovertible verification via a blood or similar test that ME exists. There have been a great number of psychological studies that illustrate how rigidly some people – especially those in positions of authority who may feel they have more to lose by admitting their mistake – stick to their first position on a given subject even when faced with clear indications that to hold this position is no longer rational. In his fascinating book, *'Irrationality, the enemy within'* Stuart Sutherland describes how people will gather all sorts of supporting views, while at the same time disregarding any arguments for the other side, so as to reinforce their primary judgement. (See especially Chapter 11, 'Distorting the Evidence'). Your doctor's dogged refusal to look at the facts regarding ME is really quite common behaviour.

But however common it may be, it is certainly not acceptable. A doctor doesn't have to be perfect but a prerequisite for an adequate patient/doctor relationship must be that you are believed and taken seriously. See below for advice on finding a new doctor.

My doctor has diagnosed ME yet keeps suggesting treatments such as counselling, cognitive therapy and anti-depressants. Do you think any of these would help or does this mean that he thinks I have a psychological, rather than a physical illness. If so, should I find a doctor who knows more about ME?

It would help to ask him rather than guess! Unfortunately, too many of us don't have a good enough relationship with our doctor to feel comfortable discussing these things. There are GPs who still believe that ME is largely a psychiatric condition and your doctor may be one of them. If this is so, it would certainly be better to find someone who is informed about the illness. Your doctor may, however, believe that ME is a physical condition but, in the absence of any treatment and in his desperation to help you, is suggesting anything he thinks might help even in a very small way. But ask yourself whether he would be suggesting these treatments if you had an uncontroversial disease like Motor Neurone Disease or arthritis? And even more to the point are they going to be of any help?

Your GP may have made these suggestions in response to you mentioning that you were finding life difficult and felt depressed. Depression can be present in ME both as a symptom and as a reaction to living with the illness and this may respond to treatment. Alternatively, you may have simply mentioned to him some of the frustration and sadness you feel about being ill. Many doctors fail to recognise these feelings for what they are – a normal reaction to a stressful and very difficult situation – and may be too ready to diagnose any expression of emotion as a sign of depression. Whether you are depressed or just feeling sad it may be worth considering what your doctor has to offer.

If as a result of being long-term ill you have become clinically depressed then anti-depressants may be very useful to you. There have also been claims that these drugs have helped some people with their ME but this is a matter of debate. People who suffer from mood swings and insomnia may find them particularly useful. Everyone responds differently to drugs; for some, anti-depressants have no, or even an adverse, effect on their health. The usual advice for ME is to start on a very low dose and build up gradually.

Counselling may well be of value as it can allow you to express and deal with the difficult emotions which are bound to crop up when living with a serious chronic illness. If you can, try to find someone who has experience of working with the physically ill as they will be in the best position to provide the right kind of empathy and support. Failing that, you need to shop around and be clear about precisely what you are looking for. Be aware that some counsellors may try to psychologise your physical symptoms so it is vital that they know – or are willing to learn – about ME. Some may also prefer to find 'solutions' to your ill health and might not be so willing for you to, say, just let off steam. Tell the counsellor at the start what your needs are and if things don't work out, do not be afraid to look elsewhere. (See below on how to find a good counsellor).

The premise of cognitive therapy is that people with ME may limit their activity not because they are physically incapable but because they *think* they are incapable. The cognitive therapist hopes to release patients from such 'negative' patterns of thought thereby effecting an improvement. For ME the treatment usually includes a programme of graded exercise. The dangers of this approach are twofold. First, people are encouraged to increase their activity without regard to how they feel physically. When you ignore a body that is telling you to stop you risk a relapse. ME sufferers do not generally have problems of doing too little but, in the vast majority of cases, tend to overdo things and suffer for it after. Overestimating what one can do without ill effect is the real problem for people with ME not the reverse. Second, taking the view that the way you think about your disease affects its progress encourages a false expectation that sufferers can somehow think themselves better. Yet the only known 'cure' at present is to avoid over-exertion and to rest. Cognitive therapy may be of value to those who have psychiatric or psychosocial problems but for sufferers who have neither of these, its value is doubtful.

Ultimately, what treatment you accept, if any, is up to you. You have the right to reject any treatments suggested to you. Trust your instincts and don't feel pressured to do anything with which you feel uncomfortable. Find out as much as possible how other people with ME – preferably with a similar history and level of illness as you – have fared with different therapies. You will have to accept that in the absence of a magic pill, suggestions of all kinds, however inappropriate, are likely to be offered. Be realistic about how much your GP will know about the latest developments in ME research. Accept that you will probably be the expert on your illness and may end up educating and updating your doctor yourself. The two ME charities produce reports and leaflets that you can show him. (See Appendix: 'Useful Addresses').

If you really feel that your doctor doesn't believe ME is a physical disease and is undermining your ability to cope, then look for someone else. Get in touch with your local group who may know of a doctor who can better respond to your needs.

Although I have been diagnosed with ME, it has been implied that my illness is due to stress. I know this can't be the reason for all my symptoms but I have, in fact, felt very stressed since I became ill. How do I know that I'm not just suffering from stress?

Think back to times of stress before you became ill. Now compare how you feel now physically with how you felt then. You should find the difference between the two rather marked. If you don't then you have been misdiagnosed!

ME has certain symptoms – particularly in very mild cases – that do bear some similarity to stress-related conditions and it wouldn't be the only disease to do so. Many illnesses feature fatigue, aches and pains, fevers, food intolerance etc. and can, in the early stages, also be confused with stress. But the severity of the fatigue in ME, the common loss of ability to perform basic functions such as walking or standing for very long, the cognitive problems, the muscle pain; all these when seen in their entirety bear little resemblance to illness caused by stress.

Although there is not yet a widely available test that can 'prove' you have ME, you do have to fit quite particular criteria – and fit them for at least six months – before a clinical diagnosis can justifiably be made. Thankfully, your doctor has not dismissed your symptoms and has recognised that you have ME.

Unfortunately, we live in a time in which all ill health – even those with diagnositic 'proof' such as cancer and AIDS – has been described at some time or another as being related to and even caused by stress. When you then actually appear to be stressed this is seized upon as evidence that you are, indeed, suffering from nothing else. But of course you are feeling stressed; you are very ill! You are probably having to take time off work if you haven't already had to give it up altogether. You are likely to have financial worries, your relationships are probably under tremendous strain, you may feel fearful about the future and anxious about getting worse and on top of all this you feel physically lousy. If that isn't a stressful situation, what is?

Even if stress played some part in your becoming ill in the first place – and this is a contentious issue – it is too late to worry about that now. What you have to do is accept your diagnosis and stop internalising others' doubts and ignorance about why you are ill, or about what your illness is. You cannot accept your diagnosis if you are constantly being undermined by others so tell them to, please, keep their opinions to themselves. It is difficult enough to cope with a disease about which so little is known without being made to feel even less secure by people telling you that you're just suffering from stress. By all means, if you are really anxious that you don't have ME seek another medical opinion, but don't be unduly influenced by people who know less about your illness than your doctor and you.

You should also try to deal with the stress you are experiencing. When you begin to feel more confident about your diagnosis and start protecting yourself from belittling remarks you will already feel less stressed. Try to recognise what other aspects of your life cause you particular stress and find a way of managing them such as relaxation, meditation or yoga. (See Appendix: 'Useful Exercises'.) Above all, make sure you do not confuse your reaction to coping with a serious illness with the illness itself.

My doctor prefers me to go to the surgery rather than make a home visit. But I often feel ill after going out to see him. Does he not have to come and see me in these circumstances?

It is up to your doctor whether he makes a home visit or not. You do not have an automatic right to one. Your doctor only has to visit you if it is necessary on medical grounds and this is open to interpretation. Because the symptoms of ME fluctuate and you are able sometimes to go to the surgery your doctor may feel that you are always up to it. He may also be unaware of how ill you feel after you have been out to see him.

Explain to him that you can occasionally get out but usually feel unwell as a result. Maybe he could arrange to drop in to see you when he is already in your area visiting other patients.

There is no point forcing yourself to go and see him if it is making you feel worse. If your doctor is completely unsympathetic to your needs, then it may be worth trying to find a more understanding one who is flexible about home visits.

I am very unhappy with the way my doctor is treating me. I am thinking of making a complaint against her. How do I go about this?

If you can, try and talk it over with her first to give her a chance to improve. If this is unsuccessful or you feel unable to do this you should write giving all the details of your complaint to the Family Health Services Authority (the address is on the front of your medical card or in the phone book). In Scotland, you should write to your local Health Board, (address in the phone book under Health Services, or the name of the Board eg. Grampian, Lothian). You must do this within a time limit of 13 weeks. The matter may be settled informally or you may be asked to attend a formal hearing. If you are not satisfied with the decision you can appeal against it within 4 weeks.

If you think your GP has behaved in an unethical or unprofessional way you can complain to the General Medical Council (See 'Useful Addresses' in Appendix). Such behaviour may include charging for free treatment, neglecting a patient, excessive drinking, breach of confidentiality, discriminatory behaviour or having a sexual or emotional relationship with a patient.

If you are not satisfied with the way your complaint has been dealt you can contact the Health Service Commissioner – also called the Ombudsman – (See 'Useful Addresses' in Appendix).

It may be helpful to approach your Community Health Council (called Local Health Council in Scotland) who can assist you in making a complaint. See Appendix for more details.

I want to change my GP. How do I do this?

You can change your doctor without giving a reason. If your present doctor is part of a practice then it is worth trying out one or two of the other doctors to see if they might suit you better. Otherwise, ask at the surgery of the doctor whose list you want to join and, unless he or she refuses to accept you, you will be added to the list. If you cannot find a GP you can contact your local Family Health Services Authority (Local Health Council in Scotland) who will allocate you a doctor. It is a better idea, however, to contact your local ME support group via the two ME charities (see 'Useful Addresses') for information of sympathetic GPs in your area.

My former GP was very ignorant about ME and believed that I was just suffering from depression. I have now been diagnosed with ME but am concerned that the notes written by my previous doctor contain incorrect information about my mental health. Can I get these notes changed?

You are entitled to have access to any medical records stored on a computer and all your written health records made after November 1991. You are also, incidentally, entitled to medical reports prepared by your doctor for your employer or insurer before they are sent on and for 6 months after the date of the report.

To see your records you must write to your GP. You may be charged a fee to see your records. You can ask the record holder to correct inaccurate or incomplete details and if they agree your records will be corrected. If they do not agree with you this should be noted in your records but you cannot appeal against their decision not to change them.

You may be refused access to your records if your GP believes it could cause serious harm to your or someone else's physical or mental health or if a third party may be identified from them. If you think that your GP has not given you proper access to your records you can complain. Your Community Health Council (Local Health Council in Scotland) can help you with this.

I want to see a counsellor. How do I find one who will be understanding about ME?

Both Action for ME and the ME Association provide a counselling service. The former offers a professional counsellor via their telephone helpline and the latter offers lay volunteers via their Listening Ear service. Another charity, Westcare, also offers professional counselling at their centre in Bristol but, obviously, this is only useful for those in their area or for a limited number of sessions for those willing to travel.

There are several other organisations that can provide counselling on specific subjects, such as Relate for relationship/ sexual problems and SPOD who run a counselling service via the telephone/letter on sexual problems encountered by people with disabilities. These other organisations may not have a great deal of knowledge about ME but they may still have something to offer and should, at the least, be willing to listen. The Samaritans can be reached over the phone at any time of day or night but, again, may not have much detailed experience with the chronically ill. Further details of these services can be found in the Appendix.

If you are looking for longer term, face-to-face counselling then you will have to find someone local. First, ask your GP who may know someone suitable. Otherwise, contact the British Association of Counselling who will send you a list of trained counsellors in your area. (See Appendix).

It is very important to check out a counsellor before you commit yourself. A sympathetic counsellor who has your best interest at heart will not mind being asked questions and should be willing to discuss what approach they use, what training and experience they have, if they have any experience with ill or disabled people and so on. Take some time to think about your needs and what you are hoping to gain from counselling and do not be afraid to discuss this with a prospective counsellor. You can interview them over the phone before you see them or arrange an initial appointment to get a feeling for how well you get on together.

Make sure that they have some understanding of ME or, at least, show a willingless to learn. It is absolutely vital for you to be reassured that they are not, through ignorance, going to explain away your physical symptoms as psychosomatic so do not shy away from discussing this issue. Make it clear how important it is that they do not make assumptions about your illness, for example that it is caused by depression, simply because you are seeking help with emotional difficulties. Tell them also if you are going to have problems getting out to see them. A good and caring counsellor will do all they can to help you and may be able to arrange home-visits or, at least, be willing to accept that you may have to cancel at the last minute.

It is important that a counsellor is clear about what you

want out of counselling. There is no point getting someone who, for example, is keen to delve into your past when all you want to do is let out some frustration about how hard it is to be ill. Get this sorted out right at the beginning as it can be difficult to extricate yourself from a relationship once counselling has begun. If you are looking for an outlet for some of the emotions you feel you can't talk to your family or friends about, make sure that your counsellor is willing and able to listen to, say, outbursts of anger on a long-term basis. Some counsellors are less interested in providing on-going support for a situation that has the potential to carry on for a very long time. It does take a particularly patient and sympathetic counsellor to allow you to go at your own pace and offer what you need rather than what they think you need.

If you find yourself involved with a counsellor who you feel is not helping you it is never too late to terminate the relationship. It can be very difficult to do this especially as it is easy to blame yourself for any problems, something that some counsellors, unfortunately, do not discourage. Talk to someone about it or even another counsellor if that helps. Do not remain with someone who makes you feel worse. A counsellor cannot change the fact that you are ill but, over time, s/he should certainly help you feel a bit better about it.

Since I became ill I have been very up and down emotionally. I think a lot about the past, something I hardly ever used to do, and I can't seem to control the feeling of turmoil that these memories bring up. It has been suggested to me that my ill health is really caused by unresolved conflicts in the past and I am now wondering if there might be some truth in this. Should I see a psychotherapist and sort myself out?

It is extraordinary how creative people can be in finding ways to 'explain' your illness rather than just accepting that you have a disease that they don't know much about. It is possible that certain events in your past drove you to develop an unhealthy life-style that could have played some part in your becoming ill in the first place. There is some debate over whether particular personality types are more prone to illness, but there have been no satisfactory conclusions. After all, we all know people who lead extremely unhealthy lives, drink too much, work too hard etc. and yet never seem to get ill at all. If emotional instability were truly the cause of serious disease our psychiatric hospitals would be full of people with serious physical illness on top of their mental illness and this is, evidently, not the case. Think back to times of emotional difficulty before you became ill. Were you severely physically ill then? If the past really had an effect on your present state of health how is it that you remained healthy for so many years before developing ME?

Having a disease that is shrouded in uncertainty and disbelief makes you all the more susceptible to self-doubt when faced with arguments that undermine the physical reality of your illness. The fact that you do feel emotionally labile seems to give credence to these arguments. But why are you feeling this way? First, studies show that many ME patients do suffer from unexplained mood swings as part of their physical condition. Second, coping with continually feeling ill as well as losing many of the things that previously kept you going, inevitably contributes to a feeling of anxiety about how you are going to manage. Third, as you say yourself, you rarely thought about the past before you became ill. You were busy living your life, filling the time working, socialising, looking after the kids, doing the housework. Now that you are unable to do some, or any, of these things you are left for the first time in your life with acres of time to think.

When you were healthy you were able to keep the past at bay. Maybe you were one of many who preferred to keep your mind as occupied as possible, rushing around, never being able to keep still. When you became ill you were forced to stop the activity, you lost a mechanism that helped keep painful memories at a safe distance. What is particularly inconvenient and difficult is that you lost this at precisely the time when you need all your emotional energy to cope with the stress and pain of becoming ill. The last thing you need when you are already in turmoil about becoming ill is to have to deal with difficult thoughts that are flooding in and demanding your attention. Yet, in a way you can't blame your subconscious. It had been suppressed and ignored for so long it couldn't help jumping at this chance, this window of opportunity when, at last, you were no longer able to distract yourself by keeping busy.

Now that you have time to think and your mind is free of distractions it can feel as if your whole past is being re-lived right before your eyes. You may remember events and emotions that you wish had remained forgotten. Worse still, some of these feelings from the past echo those brought about by being ill. Memories such as being lonely as a child reverberate deeper now that you are losing friends; memories of being rejected in the past intensify the feelings of rejection that you may now be experiencing as a result of having ME.

Many people who find themselves in situations of enforced inactivity, either through illness or captivity, experience this flooding of memories and these can feel so intense that it seems hardly possible to think about anything else. It can be very frightening to feel that you are no longer in control of your own thoughts, especially at a time when you are losing control over other aspects of your life. When others suggest that ME isn't really a physical illness but simply a manifestation of mental disturbance, it can be easy to believe them when you feel so overtaken with emotions you have never previously experienced.

There is no harm in seeing a sympathetic counsellor with whom you can share your thoughts. It might help to off-load some of your more painful memories. But exploring your past in great depth with a psychotherapist is something quite different. Psychotherapy requires great physical and emotional stamina, something that ME sufferers are unlikely to have in abundance. A person usually meets with their psychotherapist at least once or twice a week, every week and, possibly, for years. Ignoring the financial costs (although limited psychotherapy is available, via referral on the NHS), this kind of commitment would exclude many, if not most, people with ME. Feeling physically weak and ill is hardly the optimum time to start delving into past traumas; you need a lot of energy to cope with what you may discover.

The best way forward is to accept that you are, at least for a while, going to feel upset emotionally. Thankfully, once your memories have had an opportunity to come out they will soon die down a bit. You won't feel consumed by thoughts of the past for ever. It is inevitable that you will feel emotionally unsteady during this time and it can come as a shock if you have previously always been a very composed person. But when you become more used to being ill, more used to leading a quieter life you will feel more stable and at peace with yourself. Try to accept your diagnosis of ME even if it is a difficult disease to have. Try not to take too much notice of others' explanations about the whys and wherefores of your illness.

People have their own reasons for proposing certain theories and they may not always have your best interests in mind.

As soon as I feel up to doing anything I overdo it and relapse. How can I learn to pace myself so that I maintain maximum fitness yet don't make myself worse?

Contrary to what some people think, ME sufferers often find it very difficult to rest and tend to overstep their limits which can have a very serious effect on their chances of recovery. It doesn't help that everyone seems to have their own opinion on the best way to manage the illness and advice from doctors can so often be conflicting. There has been some talk in the medical profession about sufferers experiencing exhaustion not as a primary symptom of an organic disease but as a result of not doing enough and becoming unfit. Even if you know this cannot be true because your legs, for example, became weak over a short period of time before you had a chance to become unfit, even the presence of such arguments can make you think twice about the way you are dealing with your illness. You may start worrying that maybe you are not being active enough even if you know from repeated experience that overdoing it makes you feel worse. This uncertainty together with the lingering atmosphere that people with ME are natural malingerers who choose to be inactive is what pushes most sufferers to drive themselves on and on, often into progressive disability.

There is a legitimate medical concern that sufferers keep as fit as possible with this disease but often the advice simply to keep going at all costs is motivated by a lack of belief that people with ME genuinely do suffer rapid muscle fatigue and that all they need to do to get better is to throw themselves back into the swing of things. Even sympathetic doctors may recommend some sort of graded exercise regime out of ignorance about the exact nature of ME. There is no point exercising your legs to strengthen them if, at the end of the day, you don't have enough energy to walk. As soon as you start to recover and regain some of your energy you will naturally increase the use of your muscles and your fitness level will return without too much trouble. The advice most sufferers need but rarely get is how to pace themselves so that they neither do too little nor too much.

The wisest person to listen to is yourself. This means learning to listen to your body. It may be hard to develop enough self-confidence to do this but in time you will get a sense of what type of activity you can manage without feeling ill afterwards. This is likely to vary according to the time of day and also, of course, depending on your state of health in a particular week. The best guideline is to do as much as you can without feeling any symptoms. There will be severely affected sufferers who have continuous symptoms even if they are lying in bed all day and here it is a matter of trying to get through the day without making any of these worse. For other sufferers a certain level of activity can be maintained by avoiding getting to the 'sickness' phase when you are desperate to lie down. If you arrive at that feeling you have done too much and will suffer for it later. If you split tasks and rest in between you should find that you are able to manage your energy better and achieve more than if you follow the more conventional method of doing things all in one go.

The main aim is to keep a sensible balance. Rest when you need to; you will soon get an idea of how much rest is required for a particular task, for example, keeping an appointment or doing the washing up. At the same time, if you really want to do something try it even if you fear that it might make you feel worse. Whereas one-offs are acceptable, making yourself continuously sick with exhaustion is not. In the end, everyone finds a level with which they feel comfortable or at least tolerable. Each sufferer has to make their own decision how to spend the balance of their energy 'account' and different people will choose to spend their energy on different things. As long as you are maximising your potential and trying to do what you can within your limits and without feeling worse for it then you won't go far wrong.

I've tried all sorts of alternative therapies with little success. How long should I walk the treadmill of trying new things in the hope of recovery?

The enduring hope of getting better drives a great many sufferers to seek out and try anything that makes a claim to help ME. There are always stories running around the ME grapevine of how this or that person was cured by some alternative treatment and, of course, when you are very ill you want to believe them. At the same time, there may be pressure from family or friends to explore all avenues to improve your health. You may feel almost a duty to try even the more cranky therapies on offer just in case they work.

The problem arises when none of the treatments you try have any positive effect. You continue to hear stories of how they have helped others from both the practitioner and other people with ME. You begin to worry about why you are the only person who seems to get no result. Even amongst sufferers there can be an unspoken atmosphere that you are, somehow, at fault if despite having tried alternative treatments you show no improvement. People who get better are regarded as 'successes' and those who remain ill for years, although not overtly called 'failures', are often met with embarrassment as if not recovering is their own fault. So many alternative therapies promise great things but when you fail to respond it is not the therapy's fault but yours. The implication that you are to blame for failing to have a good response to treatment can drive you on to try another one, and then another in the hope that maybe next time you will have some luck.

But with each therapy that fails to help, your anxiety becomes more acute. Whereas you may have started with the more traditional and reputable complementary therapies such as homeopathy or acupuncture you begin trying things at the fringe end of alternative therapy that under more normal and less pressured circumstances you would never even consider. It is difficult to resist the temptation to try absolutely anything so long as you have heard some testimonial, however unsubstantiated, that claims a positive result. You can get to the stage where, in your desperation to get better and prove to yourself that you are not beyond redemption, you feel you can no longer afford to take a rational approach in your search for a cure. While your head may be telling you that is is impossible that this particular treatment could possibly be beneficial to any ill person your heart is clamouring; but what have I got to lose?

Unfortunately, the answer may be; quite a lot. Not only are some of these 'treatments' positively dangerous and expensive there is also the potential psychological damage to consider. Many sufferers find themselves quite obsessed with the world of alternative therapy, ceaselessly trying out the latest fad, sticking to 'treatments' that are achieving absolutely no result apart from an overdraft, out of nothing more than superstition. They may feel overcome with fear that if they stop the continuous search for a cure that some miracle will pass them by and they will have only themselves to blame if they never recover.

Life is difficult enough with ME without feeling you have to spend your last drop of energy chasing that elusive cure. Whatever you may be promised by people attempting to sell you the latest panacea for ME, there is no magic pill for the disease. If there was you would be sure to hear about it in the papers. Such a treatment would hardly be overlooked by pharmaceutical companies; there's a lot of potential money to be made out of curing over 150,000 ME sufferers in Britian alone. Your best chance of recovery is to rest sensibly, avoid over-exertion, keep to a balanced diet and develop a stategy for coping. By all means try a few of the better known therapies; they may help alleviate some of your symptoms but if you have not found any benefit from them after 3–6 months at the most, then stop them. Try not to make getting better the only focus of your life. You may be ill for a long time and it would be tragic to put the rest of your life on hold running after a cure that doesn't exist. The best way to view complementary therapies is as just that; complementary to your other efforts to manage this illness.

7

Family

*I used to get on okay with my family but since I've been ill my rela-
tionship with them has really deteriorated. Not only are they
unsupportive but some of them are actually cruel. Why have they
become like this?*

We all like to think that if something awful happens in our life
our family will be there for us but, sadly, quite the opposite often
occurs. When you become seriously ill your relationships are
put to the test. It can be extremely distressing to discover that at
a time when you need them most, your family is not only
unsympathetic but some of them are outright nasty and unkind.

Long-term illness puts a great strain on even the best relationships. It is always easier to keep even a rocky relationship
going when there are no external pressures on it. When you
were well and independent you could find a *modus vivendi* with
your family. You were able to talk about more everyday matters
such as your work and so on. When you became ill your relationship changed. Whether or not you have actually asked
them for much help, now you find yourself in the position
where you are needy. Your family may feel anxious about
possible demands being made on them. They may feel that
they should help more but fear being taken over by your illness
– and then feel pangs of guilt for not wanting to get involved.

Whereas it wasn't so difficult to maintain a reasonable relationship when life was running smoothly, as soon as problems
appear small cracks you could previously paper over start to
turn into gaping ravines. The foundations upon which your
family is built may not be stable enough to cope with any extra
stress such as one of its members becoming chronically ill. Your
relatives may find your disease frightening, threatening or
even distasteful. They may care about you but do not know
how to express it or fear that if they do express it they will be
sucked into a commitment they do not want. The stress of
illness in a family can bring old tensions to the surface and

divide loyalties. To keep the family unit intact you – the desta-biliser – may have to be pushed away and even forced out.

This happens in a subtle way. Your family may develop a new coldness towards you. This can be extremely hurtful at a time when you most need warmth and love. Their apparent hard-heartedness is one way that your family can keep your suffering at a distance. By refusing to acknowledge the severity of your situation or by accusing you of wanting to take over their lives, they can avoid thinking about your needs and hence about their responsibilities to you. To alleviate any guilt they may feel, they need to push you away and demonise you. Or if they do offer to help they may treat you like an infant, telling you what to do and refusing to see that you are capable of making decisions or knowing how best to manage your life.

Your family may hardly be aware that they are treating you this way. They may justify their behaviour by telling you that they are only, 'trying to help'. It is very difficult to challenge your family when they mistreat you. First, because, knowing you so well, they are expert in pushing your 'crumple buttons', in knowing exactly how to get to you and put you down. Second, they always have the get-out that you are, as usual, just being 'over-sensitive'.

If you have supportive parents there may be a problem of jealousy from siblings who think that you are getting unde-served, special treatment because you are ill. They fail to recognise all the things they have in their own life and overlook all the things that you have lost. All they can see is that, maybe, you are getting something extra than they are; a bit more atten-tion, a little financial help and so on. It can be very painful to witness a brother or sister actually expressing envy and resent-ment about your receiving help when your life has been so devastated by illness.

It can seem unbelievable that your family feel able to hurt you so profoundly when you are at your most vulnerable. How can the people closest to you kick you when you are down? But they are unlikely to see it this way. From their perspective, you are the trouble-maker, you are the one who won't get better, who is miserable all the time (even if you make an enor-mous effort to put on a front for them), who makes demands on them to be caring. The members of your family who are cruel to you reveal a complete lack of empathy for what you are going through. They feel it is okay to say what they like because they do not believe or see that you are going through that much. Why should they treat you any differently? It's not as if ME is a *serious* disease. They are unlikely to have any conception that when you are ill you cannot brush off hurtful remarks in the same way as when you were fit and strong. They do not begin to think about the effect of what they say in the context of a life that takes all you've got just to survive. They don't realise that just one insensitive remark can push you over the edge into depression and that it may take you weeks to recover.

It is especially hard dealing with pain that is inflicted by those you had most hoped would give you love and understanding. If someone you don't know that well treats you badly it is not such a loss to cut them out of your life. But how can you cut out your family, the people who are part of you?

First, it can help if you confront your family. Tell them individually that you feel very unhappy with the way you have been getting on. Ask them to tell you how they feel about your illness and say that if they are anxious about it you would much prefer that they were direct rather than taking it out on you by blaming or being mean to you. Say that if they do care about you being ill that you would be happy if they showed their concern even in small ways. Some people find it much easier to help in practical ways such as picking up library books or getting some shopping rather than listening and offering emotional support.

If your family treat you as a child by dominating you in a way they never did when you were well, tell them clearly and firmly that you are still quite able to make decisions; you may get upset because you are ill and find life very difficult but you are still an adult and you know best how to conduct your affairs; you are grateful for any help or support they can offer but that it has to be done in such a way that allows you some control over your life.

If you have done all this and are convinced that they do know how ME affects your life (as much as any non-sufferer can), and yet still continue to treat you badly, then you should tell them how painful you find their remarks. Even if they deny what they have done you shouldn't keep your hurt and anger to yourself. You have nothing to lose – if they refuse to even acknowledge what they are doing you will have to reduce contact with them anyway. They might as well know how you feel and you are, at least, giving them the opportunity to change. If they will not change and you feel you can cope with continuing to see them, make it absolutely clear that you will not talk about your illness and that you do not want to hear any of their opinions about it. If they refuse to comply and you always end up feeling worse after any contact with them, you will then have to make the painful but necessary decision to protect yourself until you are stronger. If you do decide to stop contact with your family, even for a short while, get as much support as you can. Find a supportive counsellor (See Chapter Six) or speak to other ME sufferers – you may be surprised to find how common these problems are.

It is obvious to me that my husband is feeling the strain of being my carer but he refuses to talk to me about it. He shuts me out by putting on a front of cheerfulness whenever he's around me. How can I show him that despite being ill I am still capable of supporting him?

It is very common for carers to experience conflicting and painful emotions toward the person they care for. Your husband may feel overwhelmed with sadness that you are ill, fearful about the future, frustrated with the routine of caring and depressed about the prospect of the situation going on and on. He may feel angry and resentful of your illness or suffocated – dreaming of escape from the pressure and respon-sibility of being a carer. He will probably also feel bad about having these feelings.

These are completely natural reactions that most carers, at some time or another, experience. But your husband may look at your suffering and feel that compared to what you are going through he has nothing really to complain about. He may feel guilty and ashamed that he sometimes wants out of the situa-tion, that he wishes you could look after yourself for a change. He may feel frightened that if he talks about these feelings all his strength and resolve will collapse and he will no longer be able to carry on.

This may be why he keeps his emotions under lock and key. He may be trying to suppress his feelings in an attempt to keep them under control and avoid confronting difficult truths.

The problem is that he won't be able to suppress them for ever. They will, at some stage, come out. If your husband can find a way of talking about his problems, about how he feels about being a carer he will probably feel better for it and despite his fears it is more likely that having got his frustrations out he will be better placed to carry on. If, on the other hand, he does not talk about his anxieties there is a possibility that they will fester and accumulate until they burst out and incapacitate him so that he cannot continue with the situation.

To avoid the possibility of this happening you have to confront your husband. Sit him down and ask him to listen to you for ten minutes without interruption. Tell him you know he can't always be feeling the way he presents himself to you. No human can be cheerful all the time, particularly under such stress. Say that you know he needs his space but you feel shut out by his relentless cheerfulness and that you miss feeling close to him. Tell him that you may rely on him for your physical needs and for some of your emotional ones too but this does not mean that you cannot contribute to your relationship. Reassure him that you are strong enough to listen to how he really feels; that you are not so fragile that you have to be protected from difficult emotions. Make sure before you say this that you really *do* feel strong enough. It can be difficult to hear someone you depend on tell you, for example, that they dream about getting away from you. Be honest with yourself about your strengths and if you feel you are not in a position to be able to listen in this way then talk about finding a counsellor for him to talk to instead.

Arrange a particular time – once a day or once a week, whatever suits you both – when your husband has a set time to talk about how he is feeling. He doesn't have to talk for very long; five to ten minutes to start with may be all that's needed. You can be flexible about it. At the beginning he may find it difficult to say anything at all but once he gets talking he may find he needs half an hour or even longer. Make sure you are physically up to listening as there is no point starting something you are not well enough to finish. When you have decided on a time, stick to it. Make it a decision between you to keep this appointment even if your husband is unaccustomed to talking this way. It may take some persuading for him to come round to thinking that sharing his problems is in both your interests. Tell him that it would help you a lot if you were able to take some of the burden off his shoulders and you would be grateful if he would just give it a try.

During the session try to listen to him as non-judgementally as possible. Do not interrupt with your own view of things or correct him. Try to avoid commenting on what he is saying; this is his time to talk not yours. This can be demanding if he is talking about how he feels about you but try to distance yourself and understand that he needs to get things off his chest. Try to see that when he is talking about you he is really talking about his fears and frustrations, about the situation rather than how he feels about you personally. Listen as attentively as you can and, when appropriate, make encouraging noises. Keep as much eye contact as possible. You can sit opposite each other, remain physically apart or hold hands – whatever you both feel most comfortable with.

Your husband, having kept his feelings to himself for so long, will probably find it difficult to get started. Help him by asking him at the beginning of the session how he feels. A good way of getting things going is to ask questions like, 'If you were a colour what colour would you be? If you were a sound, what would it sound like? If you were an animal what kind of animal would you be at this moment? How would your face look if it expressed exactly how you feel inside?' You may both feel a little awkward at first but if you can encourage your husband to express his feelings through his face or through a sound, the words will come out more easily.

Once he sees that you *can* cope with what he is saying without crumbling into an emotional heap your husband will hopefully begin to feel confident that despite being ill you can still support him. When he recognises that you have this strength he may be more willing to share his thoughts with you on a less formal basis – although keeping a set time to talk may still be the best way of ensuring he does share his feelings regularly.

Since I became ill with ME I rarely feel in the mood for sex – I find it just too exhausting. I'm worried that by constantly refusing my husband I am going to drive him away. What should I do?

When you are ill it is perfectly natural for sex to be at the bottom of your body's list of priorities. It is diverting all its energy into dealing with the disease – hence your low libido. This is made worse by the fact that being ill can also make you feel unattractive. You may not have the energy to look as good as you can. You may be so exhausted that washing your hair or even getting dressed is too much for you. You are unlikely to feel very sexy either if you are in pain or feeling down. Remember too that making love is a form of exercise. If you find walking to the corner shop arduous you are unlikely to feel up to engaging in sexual athletics.

Your husband, on the other hand, may still have a healthy sex-drive and a need to express it in some way. The important thing is to talk to him about the way you feel. Even if you think he knows, explain to him your physical limitations. There are many ways of enjoying your sexuality that do not use up as much energy as intercourse. We all feel pressure to conform to what we think everyone else is doing in bed but you may be surprised to discover that many perfectly healthy people stray from 'the norm' for all kinds of reasons.

Your husband may also need to feel that you still see him as a sexual partner and not only as a carer. Reassure him that you do still love him and find him attractive even if you cannot make love in the way you used to. Above all, try to maintain some physical communication such as hugging, kissing and holding hands. It is important to keep even small embers glowing over the lean times. (See Appendix for useful books and addresses.)

My partner is sick of being my carer. During an argument, she said that I'm always ill and if I don't get better soon she's going to leave. I don't think I could cope without her. What can I do?

There's no doubt that it can be a strain looking after someone who is ill. It may not be as trying as *being* ill, but it has its own problems nonetheless. Part of the difficulty is that a carer, unlike the person who is ill, has the choice – hard as it may be to make – of relinquishing their role and getting out of the situation. This choice can make it tough for someone to stay in a relationship that long-term illness may have changed beyond all recognition.

Few people think that they will end up looking after their partner especially when they are still relatively young. The pressure of playing a role that one wasn't prepared for can easily tarnish a formerly good relationship. Your partner may never have reckoned with the responsibility of being a carer and her anger and resentment over the restrictions your illness has placed on her life are now coming to the surface.

It may be that all she needs is an outlet for this anger and frustration. She may feel guilty for feeling this way and is passing her guilt on to you by blaming you for always being ill and threatening to leave unless you get better. Hearing this is very painful and frightening. Your partner has reminded you of your vulnerability. You may already be only too aware of how much you rely on her and how grim the prospect is of coping on one's own with ME.

It is important to try to understand your partner better and what motivates her to behave this way. Take a look at Chapter Five of *Living Creatively with Chronic Illness* by Wheeler and Dace-Lombard (see 'Useful Books' in Appendix) which examines in some detail how each person feels in a carer/patient relationship. By getting some idea of what she is feeling right now, you are in a better position to distance yourself somewhat from her rejection and see that she is, maybe, hitting out against her role as a carer rather than at you directly. Her behaviour may well be a cry for help.

Try to show her that you may be dependent on her for many things but that you can also contribute to your relationship. If you can, take a more active role in your own care by finding additional avenues of support. This may be in the form of respite care so that your partner gets a break or in the form of extra help around the house to ease the burden of more practical matters. Contact your local Crossroads Care Attendant Scheme who may be able to help you and, if you have one, your local Volunteer Bureau who may be able to provide people to assist with things like gardening or taking you out on trips and so on. Your local Social Services can also provide a range of services if they think you need them such as respite care and home helps which would also lift some of the responsibility from your partner. (See Chapter 10 for how to approach your local Social Service Department and Appendix for useful addresses.)

Encourage your partner to meet with other carers. No one can manage alone. The ME Association has a carers' network and your local support group will almost certainly be able to put her in touch with other carers in your area. Talking to other people in a similar situation may support and sustain her so that she feels more able to stay in the relationship and carry on.

Finally, tell her how you feel about her. Sometimes a carer needs to feel that she is something other than just an appendage to the ill person. However needy and dependent you are, try to give her as much space as possible. Encourage her to do her own thing, take up interests and so on. Don't forget to tell her that you love her and that you don't just see her as your carer. That you know things haven't worked out the way either of you would have planned and that it must be very difficult for her and that you will try and support her and contribute in any way you can. Finally, tell her how important she is to you and that you want to stay together not just because you are ill and are reliant on her but because you care about her and that she is still special to you.

I have been very ill for some years now and I'm not sure when or even if I will recover. When I say this to my family they tell me I'm being pessimistic. They seem almost more afraid than I am that I won't get better. How can I convince them that I'm just trying to be realistic?

In the first few years of illness you probably shared with your family the hope – and maybe even the conviction – that you would soon be well again. But after several years of illness and the passing of various deadlines for recovery you begin to realise that living with the constant hope and expectation that you will recover cannot be sustained. You learn to accept that you do not know what the future holds and that in the meantime you need to get on with your life. Like your family, you fear the future and the possibility that you may be ill for a very long time yet unlike them you come to the point when you can no longer make getting better the main focus of your life. You realise that in order to cope you have to look to the present and stop worrying about things over which you have little control. To do so means coming to terms with the uncertainty of the future and the possibility that it may not bring recovery. Facing such a prospect, painful as it is, takes away the fear and enables you to concentrate on making the most of what you have now.

Your family have different needs. Like you, they fear the future but from a different perspective. They may find it very painful to see you so incapacitated, they may feel disappointed that things have not turned out the way they would have hoped. They may feel that they cannot face a future in which you are permanently disabled, they may fear the potential responsibilities and the effect these may have on their lives.

Whereas you need to look to the future and feel unafraid of being ill for a long time, your family cannot bear to look ahead in this way. They can only countenance a future in which you are well. They see your illness as an aberration, as something to recover from not get used to. They cannot bear to even hear that you may want to accept this illness as part of your life. To them, this seems like being defeatist, that you no longer place getting better as top priority. This is why they tell you that you are being pessimistic. They fear that you have given up on becoming well and that you are willing to make do with being ill. Because your family can still get on with their lives, even if they have been deeply affected by your illness, they do not understand your need to find a way of coping with long term, severe illness. They do not understand that refusing to hold your life to ransom to an unknown future is a positive and brave step for you – that it means you are prepared to make something of your life despite severe limitations.

You need to explain to your family that when you express your uncertainty about the future it doesn't mean that you don't want to get better or that you have lost all hope. Tell them that you need to be realistic about your chances of recovery because having false hope only hurts you more and makes coping even more difficult. Tell them that you don't necessarily expect them to agree with your way of managing your illness but that you would appreciate their tolerance. Tell them that it hurts you when they say that you are being pessimistic. Explain that, on the contrary, you are being optimistic in the sense that instead of just waiting for recovery you want to live your life in the present as fully as you are able. And the emotional energy you save from no longer constantly agonising over whether or not you are going to get better will, if anything, foster a speedier recovery.

8

Friends

Before I became ill I never used to have problems getting on with people but now I find almost any social interaction awkward. I often feel like giving up socialising altogether as more often than not it makes me feel both physically and emotionally worse. Is it really worth trying to keep my crumbling social life together?

Even someone with the greatest social skills would find socialising when they are ill very difficult. Situations that you wouldn't previously have given a moment's thought to become fraught with unforseen complications when you become ill; and the more ill you are the more problematic these situations become.

There are fewer problems to overcome if you are still able to get out to socialise but there will still be some difficulty. If you are unable to work this will immediately set you apart. Even if some of your friends are unemployed, their situation remains quite different from being unable to work due to ill health. Unlike you, your unemployed friends can still lead an active life and have the opportunity to work in a voluntary capacity or keep busy looking for jobs.

While your friends are able to talk with ease about what they are doing – their hopes for their careers and so on – you can be left feeling that you have nothing much to contribute to the conversation. You are likely to feel uncomfortable because, being unable to work, you may believe that you are doing nothing of use or interest. Your friends may ask what you are doing and you feel embarrassed to tell them that you pass the time with what they may regard as leisure activities. They may think it's just great to be able to read or watch TV all day.

Then there is the problem of wanting to avoid always explaining about ME and yet at the same time needing your friends to have some understanding so they know why you are not able to do much. You do not want to feel that you have to avoid the subject of being ill completely because, after all, this is what you spend most of your energy dealing with.

The pressure of feeling you have to explain ME to your friends with the accompanying fear that they may not be very sympathetic or may even be disbelieving and undermining, can make you feel on edge and unable to relax. If their reaction to your illness is bad you may feel that if you want to see them again you will have to keep quiet about being ill. Having to put on a front continuously, especially when you are feeling unwell, is a tremendous strain. It can also be very demoralising to have to pretend to be something you are not in order to be accepted. This pretence – when both you and your friends know you are ill but just avoid mentioning it – puts a distance between you and your friends that is often difficult to bridge. You feel unable to be yourself because of the tacit agreement that illness is simply not to be discussed. How can you be yourself if you have to keep hidden half of what you are?

If your health prevents you from getting out on a regular basis, just keeping a social engagement can be a problem. A straightforward invitation to come to dinner the following week turns into an ordeal. You spend the days leading up to the event in a constant state of worry; will you be able to make it? Should you ring and cancel now or wait until the day and then cancel if you're not well? But if you leave it to the last minute to maximise your chances of being able to go, what will your friends think if you have to cancel at such short notice? The anxiety of not knowing whether you will be well enough to keep the engagement never mind have enough energy to sit through the actual dinner starts to outweigh the advantage of going at all. You may begin to feel that it simply isn't worth the worry and decide to avoid the stress of socialising altogether by rejecting any future invitation. Or more likely you will decide to accept the invitation but end up cancelling anyway and find that, over time, the invitations start to dry up.

The iller you are, the more difficult social interaction becomes. You may be housebound but still have friends who are willing to come over and see you. But if you are so ill that you cannot get out of the house, you are also likely to be so ill that just a little company completely exhausts you. Because you do not know if you will be up to seeing anyone on a particular day you can end up having to cancel even people coming to see you in your own home.

Unless you see friends fairly regularly the atmosphere between you is bound to become awkward. Ease in friendships comes out of shared lives, shared interests, shared values. When you become ill your life can change so radically that you can lose much of what you previously had in common with your friends. Your lives may now be so different that it can be difficult to find enough mutual experience to rebuild a new relationship.

Taking into account all the problems of seeing friends when you are ill, it has to be a personal decision whether or not you feel the benefits outweigh the drawbacks. If you possibly can, try to hold on to your friends because once you have lost them it can be very difficult to make new ones – particularly if you are unable to work or are housebound. They may not be very understanding about your illness, your relationship may not be as good as it was, you may have to put on a front whenever you are with them, but even all this has to be preferable to complete isolation. Cut out the friends who are really hopeless, who make you feel worse about being ill and concentrate on those who are willing to find some middle ground upon which you can maintain some sort of friendship.

As I'm rarely up to seeing people most of my contact is over the phone. The problem is that I find I get really nervous and can't think of anything to say. I never used to be self-conscious on the phone so why is it so difficult now?

Because you are ill the phone has taken on a completely different role in your life. Before, you could take it for granted because it was only one of many ways of communicating with people. Now it has become almost your only way of keeping in touch with others and this puts a pressure on each phone call you make.

You never used to feel self-conscious because the phone never used to be your main point of contact with friends. You probably used it to make arrangements to go out and meet rather than for long conversations. If you think back you are likely only to have had long talks on the phone with people you knew very well and felt especially comfortable with. You probably still feel okay phoning these people. Now think about who you have attempted to have long conversations with since you've been ill. You may have lost several, if not all, of your acquaintances and more superficial friends when you stopped being able to go out and socialise. These friendships may have been replaced by other people with ME whom you may never have actually met and with whom, apart from ME, you may have little in common. But because your whole social life depends on the telephone you have higher expectations from these sorts of relationships than you would under normal circumstances. This is why you often feel nervous and at a loss for words. It can be very stressful speaking to people you hardly know when you can see neither their face nor their body language. The telephone can be a very intense medium to use for conversation – any silences can feel much more embarrassing than they would in a face-to-face situation.

It may be that you are attempting to turn a friendship that was originally based on going out for a light-hearted chat to the pub into one in which you talk about how you are feeling and what life is like being ill. It will inevitably feel like an uphill struggle if you try to force what was only a fun and superficial relationship into one which is supportive and close.

On top of this, you will be feeling exhausted most of the time. Before ME, how conversable did you feel when you had the flu? When you are used to feeling ill all the time it is easy to forget why you often feel tense and stretched by the exertion of socialising. Talking on the phone is always more demanding when you are sick and weak than when you are fit and full of energy.

Losing friends and being unable to participate in a normal social life can easily dent your self-confidence. Sometimes you can forget that your problems are caused by being ill and you can start to believe that they are something to do with your personality. This lack of self-esteem can make you feel even more nervous about making contact with others. You may feel you have to fill all the spaces in the conversation, be witty and entertaining so that you won't lose more friends. And yet you don't have the energy or, maybe, the confidence to carry this through. Feeling that you have to project an acceptable front and always say the right things so that people will continue to keep in touch puts a tremendous burden on a conversation. It's not surprising that you then start to dread using the telephone at all.

If your only point of contact is through the phone, however, you do have to find a way of managing your social life this way.

The first thing to do, if you can, is to get an answer-phone. This way you can control when you use the telephone so that you don't end up talking when you are not really up to it. Only by making calls when you are feeling reasonably well will the conversation feel less stressful. Second, accept that some relationships are just not going to thrive over the phone. Be realistic and focus on those friendships that display the greatest potential.

Make sure also that you are not just listening to people's problems over the phone. For some people the telephone becomes a kind of confessional and you can end up as the counsellor. If you want to offer to listen to people do so in a structured setting such as the ME Association's Listening Ear service where it is explicit what you are doing. Counselling people when there is no acknowledgement that this is what is happening may be one of the reasons why you are finding yourself tensed up before and after phonecalls. Likewise, don't end up talking only about your problems for the entire call either. There is nothing wrong with mutual support but if either of you continually dominates the conversation with your problems it is fairer to talk to a counsellor.

There is a skill in using the telephone and this needs developing if, like most people, you are unused to using it for all your social needs. One technique is to keep the conversations short and don't be too afraid if there are pregnant pauses. If the person at the other end of the line refuses to fill any at all then you will have to decide if they are really worth struggling to talk to.

Finally, think about writing letters to supplement your phoning. There are some very good penfriend/friendship clubs around. (See Appendix for addresses). Some sufferers have problems writing but once you have made contact you can always record your 'letter' on a cassette and correspond that way. Correspondence is a lot less demanding than the phone. You can choose when you want to write and take time over what you want to say. You can stop and start as many times as you want and, of course, it is a lot cheaper!

A close friend recently told me that I have become very negative since I developed ME. This really hurt as I thought I was being quite cheerful in front of him. How can I face him if he feels that way about me?

It is very hurtful when friends say this sort of thing. It is certainly not very friendly or kind. When you become ill you are bound to change to a certain extent. I suspect that your friend is finding these changes rather difficult and is blaming you rather than having to explore his deeper feelings about you being ill.

If your life has been quite severely altered by ME your friend may be finding it hard to come to terms with the fact that much of what you used to share, for example being able to go out together, chat about work, mutual friends and so on, is now impossible. He may feel angry that your illness has changed your relationship and this anger comes out as irritability. Each time you mention ME he is reminded of the change in your friendship, feels more irritable and takes it out on you. He may be feeling anxious about where your relationship is going and what is expected of him. He may feel that he doesn't want to carry on a friendship with someone who has long-term problems and may then feel guilty about this. Calling you 'negative' allows him to blame you for his difficult feelings.

Or he may genuinely believe that you are being negative due to ignorance about how seriously ill you are. Unless someone has been long-term ill themselves they can find it hard to avoid interpreting a straightforward description of your daily life – which is inevitably full of problems – as just 'being negative'. His relationship with you was based on the 'old you' not the you who is ill. He may be trying to maintain this image of you by carrying on the friendship as if nothing has changed. He may be framing his questions about your life in such a way that forces you always to respond in the negative. He may ask, for example, if you have seen this friend or been to that party to which – because you are too unwell to do so – you have to reply 'no'. Avoiding the subject of your illness and by extension how things have changed for you he may continue to discuss only those aspects of your life in which you can no longer participate. When you then respond that you can no longer do these things he accuses you of being negative.

You may be feeling very low about the difficulties you are facing and may have sought his support by telling him how you feel. By accusing you of being negative he is keeping you and your problems at a distance; saying, in effect, that he does not want to hear your pain. It is challenging to hear about the devastation illness can wreak on a life and he may feel that while he can cope with more everyday problems he can't or just doesn't want to face such major ones. It does require more work to keep a relationship going through long-term invalidity and some people simply prefer not to make the effort.

Whatever your friend is feeling, being called negative is something you should stand up to. Tell him how hurt you are and that you had, in fact, been making a special effort not to appear that way in front of him. Tell him that you can understand some of the reasons why he may think you are negative but that you disagree with him. Explain to him that what he sees as negative is just you coping with a difficult situation and that if he were in the same position he would, in all likelihood, act in a similar way. Tell him that you are dealing with a lot of changes in your life and that you can't be expected to be as easy-going as you used to be and that you hope he can take this into account.

You have then to decide if there is still potential for a friendship here. If you think there is, you may have to accept that if you talk too much or even at all about illness this particular friend is unlikely to stick around for very long. ME may be a big part of your life but, hard as it is to swallow, many people won't want to make it a part of theirs too – particularly if it looks as if you're going to be ill for a long time. To keep your friendship going you may have to resign yourself to making even more of a special effort to avoid talking about life with ME – even if you don't have much of a life outside this – and concentrate instead on what your friend is doing and his life. It has to be your decision whether a friendship based on this sort of inequality is worth saving.

It may be that all you and your friend needs is a good heart to heart and that by explaining how much stress you are under, he will become more understanding. If you ask him to make allowances for you he may become less judgemental and accepting of you. In time, he may stop seeing only your illness and recognise that you are still, in the most important ways, the person you always were.

When I sit in the garden my neighbours make comments like, 'It's all right for some'. Now I feel bad about having any enjoyable moments while I'm ill despite the fact that most of my life is a real struggle.

Comments like these are made out of ignorance; of the fact that you are ill in the first place or that illness – despite sometimes being able to sit out in the garden while others work – is anything but enviable. Unfortunately, these kind of comments serve only to remind you how different you are. They make you feel all the more self-conscious that you are not part of the normal run of things. If you have already been undermined about ME they can lead to a feeling that maybe you should never be allowed to have a nice time while you are ill, that somehow it isn't quite right. After all, you're supposed to be suffering from a debilitating disease aren't you?

This is plainly ridiculous yet it doesn't stop many ill people feeling this way. It is hard not to internalise the stereotype that people with ME are malingerers who love just sitting around in the garden all day doing nothing. But why shouldn't you try to get as much pleasure out of your life as you can? Being ill doesn't mean you shouldn't enjoy yourself. In fact, you have all the more reason to seize the moment as your life is normally so difficult. People who are healthy don't feel guilty about having a nice time so why should you? Just because you may be on Benefit and have been classified as ill or disabled doesn't mean you have to adhere to others' views of how you should appear or feel bad about getting some pleasure out of the generally miserable experience of ME.

If you can face it and you think it might make you feel better you could try to challenge your neighbours. When they say 'It's all right for some' you could reply by saying, 'Well, unfortunately I'm long-term ill but it is nice to get some fresh air' or something to that effect. What will make you feel even better, however, is if you are able to develop a sense within yourself that regardless of what others think you have a right to do what you want with your life, that you deserve to get as much out of it as you can regardless of your circumstances and that what you do is really nobody's business but your own. If you can really come to believe this then your neighbours' comments will lose their power to hurt you.

I hate telling people I have ME as they invariably have a distorted idea of what it is. How will I ever come to terms with this disease if I can't even bear to mention its name?

ME is notorious for being known by a host of different names.

Argument still rages over whether it is best called ME, Chronic Fatigue Syndrome, Post-viral Syndrome to name just three. Even more confusing is that these labels are also used by different people to describe different conditions. The fact is that fatigue syndromes are very common. Unfortunately some of these, which may be caused by a variety of things including stress, unhealthy life-style or candida, are misdiagnosed as the clinical condition, 'ME' by doctors unfamiliar with the quite strict criteria a patient has to fulfill for a diagnosis. The label, 'ME' therefore becomes no more than an umbrella name for a variety of conditions that may have quite different symptoms and causes yet that all share the symptom of fatigue. And the word, 'fatigue' can be used to describe vastly different experiences. In ME it can mean that you cannot walk more than 100 yards once a week, make a meal or even dress yourself. With a stress-related fatigue syndrome it can mean that after working all week you don't feel up to going out in the evening or you feel tired all the time.

So when you tell people that you have ME the meaning of the term is diluted by the fact that it is misused to describe conditions that are very different. It is as if the term, 'stomach ache' was commonly used to describe any condition – from chronic indigestion to stomach cancer – that shared the symptom of pain in the stomach. If you had the latter but only had the umbrella name of 'stomach ache' to describe it you would find that every time you told people you would be met with comments like, 'oh, I've had that' or, 'that's nothing very serious' when, in fact, what they are describing is chronic indigestion! This is exactly what happens with ME. Because many people are misdiagnosed or incorrectly diagnose themselves there are a plethora of people out there who, when they say they have had ME and have been 'cured' by changing their diet, or have ME and can still go hill-walking and work full-time, muddy the public's understanding of a disease that for those who really have it, can be very serious indeed. In this context it is not suprising that others have a distorted idea of what ME is really about.

Having no clear label to describe your illness properly, like other diseases, is profoundly unsettling. The significance that labels play in constructing a person's identity is often taken for granted. Yet human culture is based on the use of labels; this person is middle-class, that person is black, he is a plumber, she is a teacher. When your life is significantly disrupted by illness and you can no longer hitch the major part of your identity onto what you do for a living, there becomes a great need to find an alternative way of describing what you are. In normal circumstances, a label is used to give others some indication of what your life is about. Because there is no label that adequately describes your illness, no label that is fixed and uncontroversial it is difficult to feel your identity as fixed or uncontroversial either – hence your feeling of acute discomfort when you tell people that you have ME.

If you had a condition with a well-known name such as MS or Cerebral Palsy a swift mention of this would usually get the desired effect. A label can never get over the complete experience of an illness or disability but it does help – particularly if you are unable to work – to provide some answer to the dreaded question, 'so what do you do?' People with more well known and undisputed labels, especially if their illness/disability is visible, often have different problems of identity. For example, it may be assumed that anyone with such a condition must have a completely empty and reduced existence when, in reality, many may lead very active lives.

With ME the opposite occurs. Any mention of this label and people – for the reasons discussed above – often assume that there is nothing much wrong with you and that you are exaggerating when you describe your incapacities. The insecurity you already feel about having an illness that even the medical profession feel confused about is then made worse by the feeling that you cannot tell people about your illness because all the labels that are available project a false and negative image of it.

If the only label you have to describe your life makes you feel worse then you have to think seriously about whether you want to use it at all. There is no reason why you should do anything that makes your life even more difficult. The truth is that unless you spend a significant amount of time explaining exactly how the disease affects your life and the person who you are telling is particularly empathetic, you are never going to get people to completely understand your situation. It is important that those with whom you have a great deal of contact, such as family and close friends, have an understanding of your illness. But in the case of those you see only from time to time, acquaintances, neighbours, the hairdresser, the woman at the corner shop etc., you have to decide whether it really enhances your life to tell them you have ME. If you feel uncomfortable using that name but, understandably, don't want to or can't pretend that you are completely well you can just as viably say that you have a viral or chronic illness or, if you want to give a bit more detail, 'a viral illness which leaves me with little energy…' Or you can say that you are in poor health but prefer not to discuss it.

There is no law that dictates that you have to tell everyone personal details about yourself. When your life changes and veers away from the norm you can feel almost obliged to explain why it has become so different. This feeling comes from within, possibly as a way of externalising your situation so as to get better used to it, but it also comes from others. If you appear unusual in any way – perhaps others notice that you are not at work or have to sit down a lot – people want to know the reason for it and they can be quite insistent. Most of us are curious and, given half the chance, like to pigeon-hole others. But it is your choice whether or not you give out information that is, after all, really rather private. In an ideal world, telling people that you are ill or have ME would present no problems, but you have to be realistic. Maybe the situation will improve one day. In the meantime, remember that it takes all sorts to make up this world and you have a perfect right to be different without having to discuss or explain your illness to anyone.

Compared to what others my age are achieving I feel I contribute nothing. I feel so useless. I am single and have been virtually bedbound for several years. I'm neither well enough to work or have a family. Is there really any reason for me to carry on?

Living with illness that severely restricts you in this way is a major challenge. You have to face tremendous emotional pain over all that you have lost and part of this pain is questioning the purpose of your life. It is hard to feel you are of any use to anyone when you are dependent on others for so many of your needs and when the things you are able to do are so small. It can be excruciating to see people, particularly those of your own age, getting on with their lives in precisely the way you would have done if only you hadn't become ill. Being an observer rather than a player in life is very hard especially when you do not know if you will ever become a player again.

There can seem little point in continuing an existence that is not only painful to yourself but also seems of little benefit to others.

Does this feeling of uselessness come only from being ill? Is being unable to participate fully in life the only reason why you should find little point in carrying on? Your life may be very painful but are there other things that make you feel your existence is pointless?

Our culture makes it very difficult for the severely ill and disabled to feel worthwhile. Its constant celebration of the successful makes it clear that doers are looked up to and onlookers are not. Even the disabled are admired as long as they are winners, either by getting better or getting something positive out of their situation.

But what if you don't have the energy to make something out of your illness? What happens if all your time and energy is used up with the task of simply getting through another day? Because 'getting by' has no end product, your life can seem empty and absurd. And what, you ask yourself, is the point of my continuing in this way if I'm not sure I'll ever get better; what is the point of survival for survival's sake?

Actually, survival is what the majority of people in the world are engaged in. Because you are surrounded by people with full and active lives who are privileged enough not to have to be concerned with survival, you can forget that there are millions of others who – maybe for different reasons from you – are also pinned down and hemmed in by the frustration and hopelessness of doing nothing but just getting by. But these people – in the slums of the Third World and the refugee camps of warring countries – do not question the point of their lives. They know the point only too well; to get through another day. This is enough of a reason to live and no further reasons are necessary.

But you question the value of just 'getting by' because you have enough food and water to keep your physical body going and this leaves you time to think about the point of your existence. Because our society is no longer based only on subsistence, finding a meaning and point in life has become of great importance. People who are perfectly fit and well are thrown into despair when they cannot find a meaning in life. And although there are many who believe there is some higher meaning and point to our existence on earth, the essential point of life is life. Or rather there is no intrinsic point – religious and ethical beliefs aside – apart from trying to live it as comfortably as possible. Ask most people what they most want out of life and they will reply, 'to be happy'.

So when you say that your life is pointless you must realise that, in essence, so is everyone else's. What you are actually saying is that living in a society that values what people do over what they are makes you feel useless.

Therefore, you don't take pride in the qualities you have had to develop to be able to manage your illness because they don't seem to have a use within society. Instead you focus on all the talents you are wasting. Although the demands of coping just one more day with ME are far greater than any you might have encountered when you were well, you feel that nothing you cope with is of importance because it doesn't have a practical application elsewhere. Even though it takes a hundred times more resilience, courage and tenacity to live with severe and long-term illness than it takes simply to go out to work, you value people who work more than you value yourself because, after all, you are only spending your energy on yourself and what is so useful about that?

But your values rest upon the assumption that everyone in life selflessly goes about their business being terribly useful and helping people along the way. Yet the majority of people work so that they earn enough money to look after themselves and their family. Applying the same rules of judgement as you apply to yourself – what is so essentially useful about working and bringing up a family? Yes, there are those who are motivated by a vision to help, to make the world a better place. But money and security for themselves and their family is the motivating factor for most people and thus the central meaning in their life.

Now we are getting closer to why you feel so useless. What brings meaning to most people's lives is bringing up the next generation, looking after themselves and those they care for, being inter-dependent and enjoying themselves. You are not able to do these things and it is this that is making you unhappy. If you are single and ill it is likely that you are going to be lonely and this contributes to your feelings of being worthless. The rejection and hurt of social isolation can on its own sap your confidence and self-esteem and lead you to feel there is no point carrying on because no one really cares about you. Add to this the emotional demands of coping with feeling continuously ill and being unable to produce anything solid that you can show to the world and it's not difficult to understand why you feel so low.

The first thing to start telling yourself is that although your efforts are unlikely to be recognised, you are developing qualities that many people could do with having but don't. Qualities such as courage, patience, toughness, thoughtfulness, the ability to appreciate small things and so on. You may get better one day and be able to put these rare qualities to good use. But you don't have to rely on getting better to feel good about coping with hardship. Although we may not be aware of it, every contact we make in this world has a ripple effect. An employer shouts at an employee who then takes it out on his wife, who then criticises her daughter, who then gets upset and kicks the dog.

The way you develop inside is important. Obviously, if you are religious then the kind of person you are will already be important to you, but even if you are not you can influence other people – whether it is the home-help, the doctor or people you write to – by the way you handle misfortune. This doesn't mean you always have to have a smile slapped on your face. But you can show people that it is possible to get something out of life even when you are so severely ill. You can share your perspective on life and give courage to others in a similar situation. Hopefully, too, seeing you struggle on against all odds will put the more everyday problems of others in perspective and make them appreciate what they have in their lives.

Remember that not everyone 'out there' working is actually being very useful. There are many jobs which involve exploitation of other people, the destruction of the environment and so on. Even people in the helping professions can often make those in their care feel worse by being unsympathetic and unkind as described earlier in this book. Many people who are active in this world spread their portion of misery around. In your more passive role you are less likely to hurt others – limiting the harm one causes in other people's lives is something several religions recognise and value.

Above all, you must try to believe that you have a right just to be. The odd thing is that while 'just being' is dismissed and even frowned upon and keeping busy and doing lots of things is admired, the first is a million times more difficult to achieve than the second. Again, there are religions such as Buddhism that acknowledge this difficulty and look up to those who are able to reduce their lives to a state of simplicity and 'just being'. But you will have to accept that in this society your efforts are unlikely to be admired. You must learn to accept your passivity for your own peace of mind and not for others' approval.

It is essential not to internalise negative attitudes to illness and disability. There are people, often proponents of voluntary euthanasia, who say, 'Well, if I were unable to look after myself and could no longer be useful I'd prefer to be dead', and although they are usually talking about terminal or progressive rather than chronic illness, there are echoes in these beliefs of the eugenic idea of 'useless mouths'. That is, that unless you are an active participant in society you are worthless. These ideas are very damaging to people who are no longer in the position of being active in life and it is very important to see them for what they are; a disrespect for the contribution – both passive and active – that ill and disabled people make to the world.

You must stop comparing your life with those of well people. You are in an entirely different situation now and you have to work with what you've got. It may be helpful to find a counsellor who can help you do this and with whom you can share some of your pain. Try very hard to stop telling yourself that you are useless or that there is no point in your life. Do you go around saying that about other people who are ill or disabled? Then you should not say it about yourself. You are here and you have a right to be here. Ill people are part of the world and they will always be part of it. Just because others have not yet come to appreciate that even the least active person is still of value, doesn't mean that you should stop valuing yourself. If you can believe that surviving another day is your right and that you don't have to justify your existence then life will feel a lot easier.

9

Work and Welfare Rights

Due to increasing ill health, I recently had to reduce my hours to working part-time yet some of my colleagues say I look too well to really be ill. How can I make them believe me?

Ask them whether just by looking at a car from the outside they can tell if it has a flat battery and explain that ME is a bit like that. You really cannot make out the condition of the internal workings of a car or a human being simply by looking at the exterior. Explain that there are many illnesses and disabilities where the sufferer doesn't look that different from anyone else. A straightforward example is someone with a back injury. If you feel they are willing to listen, tell them about ME but don't feel you have to defend your illness. It is hard having a disease about which there is a lot of ignorance but you have nothing to be ashamed of. It may be easier to hand out some leaflets from one of the ME charities instead and offer to answer any questions later.

Some of your colleagues may be genuinely confused when they hear you say you are ill and yet cannot see that you look any different from themselves. They may be sincerely interested in finding out about ME and be happy for you to tell them about it. Others will believe what they want to believe regardless of what you tell them. Explain once but do not keep on explaining. When people have the information it is their decision whether or not they are going to change their minds on the basis of it or maintain their prejudice. You cannot force people to believe you but you can ask them to keep their opinions to themselves.

After a long spell of illness my health seems to be improving. How soon should I think about returning to work?

It is very tempting to rush back to work as soon as you feel a bit better. The pressure to get back is compounded if your job is still being held open for your return. You may fear that if you stay away too long your employer will sack you. Your chances of having your job waiting for you when you get back after a long period of sick leave depends on a number of factors: the size of the company/organisation, whether or not they have a sympathetic policy towards people with ME, how long you have worked there and the prognosis they receive from your doctor on how long you are likely to be off work. The larger the organisation the more willing your employer should be to keep your job open, or at least find alternative, lighter work that you may be able to manage. There are no hard and fast rules on this issue but if you feel that you have been unfairly dismissed seek advice from your local employment advice centre or union representative.

Even if you don't have a job to return to there are other reasons for wanting to get back to work as soon as possible; emotional, financial and practical. Returning to work signifies that things are going to be 'normal' again, it signals the end of feeling like a spare part, of having no function. It means no longer having to be dependent on the state, being able to afford things again. It means getting out from under your family's feet, feeling back in control and independent.

But hurrying back to work prematurely is counter-productive. You must be sure that you are well enough not only to be able to get through the first few weeks but to have the stamina to continue working week in, week out and indefinitely with no ill effect. In their eagerness to get back to work, many sufferers convince themselves that they are fit enough because they can now go out and do the shopping and manage the housework. They fail to remember how demanding the commitment of work is and that once you have gone back after a lengthy period of sick leave your employers are hardly going to take it kindly if you then become ill again.

Before you make such a commitment it is better to test exactly how well you are by doing some voluntary work. Gradually increase your hours and continue for at least a few weeks if not a month or two. Only when you can manage this with no problems should you start thinking about returning to paid employment. It may be hard for you to hold back from going back to work the minute you start to feel better. You may feel that you should be earning your money by now and not still be relying on the welfare state. Your doctor may also feel that if you are well enough to work voluntarily then you are well enough to work and be paid for it. But you must tell your doctor – and yourself if necessary – that this is only a short term measure to assess your ability to cope physically with the rigours of employment. Tell your doctor that you cannot afford to jeopardise your recovery by returning to work too early but that, of course, you are wanting to get back as soon as you are sure you are fit enough.

Beware, however, your ability to do voluntary work without losing benefit depends on which benefit you are receiving. On Income Support you are allowed to do up to sixteen hours a week voluntary work without it affecting your benefit. On Disability Living Allowance you are allowed to work full time, so working voluntarily isn't a problem. But on Incapacity Benefit and Severe Disablement Allowance the voluntary work you are allowed to do has to be 'therapeutic work'. This basically means work that will help your recovery or prevent further deterioration of your health. What kind of work is deemed 'therapeutic' is open to interpretation by both your doctor and your local DSS adjudication officer. To take up this kind of 'therapeutic work' (which must be for less than sixteen hours a week on average and from which you earn no more than £44 a week) without losing benefit you will need your GP's support as it has to be done on his/her specific advice. It should be argued that voluntary work will help to prevent your ME getting worse, ie. by testing your ability to work without risk of a relapse. If the amount or kind of work you are participating in makes your inability to find paid employment questionable (ie. you are doing the same kind of work that you could get paid for) you may be asked to attend a DSS medical to assess if you are still unfit to work.

I have been off school for a couple of years and although I've had tuition at home I'm badly behind in my school work. My GCSE's are next year and I'm terrified that I'm not going to be in a position to take them. What should I do?

It can be very frightening to feel that you are getting behind at school and that you may not make it to your exams. It is often drummed into children from an early age how important exams are and how one's whole career rests on what qualifications you get. Of course, people with qualifications do get a head start but exams are not the be-all and end-all. There are plenty of people who have never passed an exam in their life who do very well for themselves and are content with their lives and vice-versa. Getting your health back on the rails is vastly more important than getting exams in terms of what quality of life you will have in the future.

But it is very hard to see all your friends getting on with their lives and getting on with school with no problems. Feeling left out and as if life is passing you by can make you feel more anxious about keeping up with everyone else – including getting your exams. It is a genuine worry to think that you may not get the qualifications you know you are capable of, and not knowing what will happen to you in the future. But fixing on a goal that you are not really up to may be a way of clinging on to a sense of normality – if you can manage to pass the same exams as your friends then you can feel as if you are not so different and that returning to school and back to 'normal' isn't really so far off. Getting behind in schoolwork seems to symbolise lagging behind in other things and only serves to make you feel even more isolated and different. But for your health's sake you will have to learn – tough as it may be – to let go of the things you had expected to achieve at your age. It is not the end of the world if you can't manage your GCSE's next year. You can always catch up later. Even if the worst comes to the worst and you don't manage to get any qualifications at all, there are plenty of ways to catch up when you are older. Being a bit more mature in years often speeds up the learning process which can make passing exams a lot easier. You need to conserve all your energies so that you stand a better chance of getting better. Saving your energy by trying to stop worrying about whether or not you will be able to keep up with your schoolmates will increase your chances of recovery and, therefore, of getting back to school sooner.

I have been off work on full pay for two months but am not getting any better. It seems unlikely that I shall be able to return to work for a while. What benefits am I entitled to both in the short and long-term?

You are entitled to Statutory Sick Pay (SSP) which is administered and paid by your employers. If you have been on full pay for two months it is likely that you are also entitled to

Occupational Sick Pay, the terms of which will be outlined in your contract of employment. You can claim Income Support (IS) from the Benefits Agency but this is a means tested benefit and how much you receive or whether or not you get it depends on your income and capital. Income Support can give you help with your mortgage and is a passport to additional benefits such as free prescriptions. It may also entitle you to receive help with rent and rates in the form of Housing Benefit and Council Tax Benefit which is claimed from your Local Authority. Your net SSP payment counts as income for IS and so reduces the amount you would otherwise get from the latter.

SSP continues for 28 weeks after which, if you are still unable to work, you should claim Incapacity Benefit (ICB). You can continue to claim IS while on ICB (ICB counts in full as income for the purposes of IS) and the long term rate of ICB will qualify you for a disablity premium on your IS.

To receive ICB you have to pass the 'all work' test which tests your ability to perform the activities set out in the regulations. Some people are exempt from this test (therefore you should seek advice before making a claim) but you will probably have to complete a questionnaire not all of which may apply to you. The 'all work' test comprises two lists, one of physical disabilities and the other of mental disabilities and unless you have become severely depressed on top of your ME only the former list will apply to you. This contains categories of activity such as 'bending and kneeling', 'walking up and down stairs', 'lifting and carrying'. For each activity there is a further list of what are called, 'descriptors'. These describe possible levels of disability within a particular category of activity and are given points according to how incapacitating the disability is considered to be by the DSS. To be treated as incapable of work you have to score a total of fifteen points from the entire physical disabilities list (and if you have severe mental problems as well – fifteen points from both the physical and mental list with a minimum of six points coming from the mental disabilities list).

The problem for people with ME is that while some sufferers may be able to walk up and down a flight of stairs once without difficulty and therefore fail to score any points on this particular test, this may not reflect the true extent of their difficulty climbing stairs. During long periods in bed, a sufferer may not be able to climb any stairs at all or even during a good spell may be able to climb the stairs but have to rest afterwards or cannot do so repeatedly without feeling ill. The 'all work' test is not well designed to cope wih conditions that fluctuate. It is, therefore, important when faced with either a 'yes' or 'no' box to tick the box that indicates yo *do* have problems performing the task in question even if you can perform it sometimes. You can then qualify your answer in the space provided and give further information about how ME affects you in relation to performing this task.

After you have completed and returned your questionnaire you will probably be sent an appointment to be examined by an Examining Medical Officer (EMO). You can ask for a home visit if you are too ill to travel. The EMO will ask you about your condition and your medical history, examine you and assess whether you pass the 'all work' test taking into account your degree of capacity in each of the specific areas of activity in the test. The EMO's assessment will not consist simply of asking you to perform these activities but should include all the information you have given on your questionnaire and told the EMO. This is important for the ME sufferer as during the examination you may be able to sit up for 10 minutes (which the EMO will take into account) but suffer for it later and have to lie down to recover. The EMO will not know this unless you tell him or her. Likewise, If s/he asks you to bend over once or twice you may be able to do so quite easily but know from experience that to do so repeatedly would make you very sick. It is vital, therefore that you tell the EMO exactly how performing each task affects you not only while you are doing it or doing it once or twice but afterwards and if you do it over a lengthy period of time. If you are having a good day on the day of your examination, make it clear what your health is like during bad days. It may help to take notes in with you to remind you what information you want to get over and/or get a friend or relative to come with you for moral support.

You can also claim Disability Living Allowance (DLA) and this benefit is not counted as income for IS purposes nor that of Housing Benefit or Council Tax Benefit. DLA has both a 'mobility' and 'care' component that can be paid at different rates either together or seperately. To qualify for the mobility component you must satisfy various conditions but the most relevant for ME sufferers is that 'you must be suffering from a physical disability such that you are virtually unable to walk'. This is the commonest route to the higher mobility rate of DLA. Obviously, this is open to interpretation but you will be deemed virtually unable to walk if your ability to walk outdoors is so limited as regards distance or speed that you experience 'severe discomfort' OR that the 'exertion required to walk would ... be likely to lead to a serious deterioration in ... health'.

It is wise to be cautious when writing on the claim form what distance you can walk. Consider carefully not what you can manage as a one-off but what you can do in a normal day. Consider what, if any, effect walking such a distance has on your health. How long it takes you to recover from any walking should be also taken into account. A classic symptom of ME is feeling terrible after minor exertion and you should expand on this in the space provided and at the medical examination that you will probably be asked to attend after the DSS have received your application. If you can occasionally walk, say, two hundred metres without ill effect but can usually manage only fifty metres then you should make this clear.

The 'care' component of DLA, the test which most severely affected sufferers will be able to meet with little problem, is the 'cooking test' where you need to show that your disability makes you unable to perform the tasks needed to cook a main meal. These include physical tasks such as bending, lifting, ability to peel and chop vegetables but also takes into account the degree of stamina required to cook such a meal. Many sufferers may be able to perform individual physical tasks such as chopping or lifting but, overall, cannot prepare a meal because of fatigue. You should pass the 'cooking test' on these grounds and be entitled to the lower rate of the 'care' component. To receive the higher rate of this component you need to satisfy conditions concerned with 'attention' and 'supervision' day and/or night and unless you require significant help with basic tasks for most of the day and/or night you may not be eligible despite being very ill. Most severely affected sufferers are, however, likely to pass the 'limited attention' condition which requires you need attention for a 'significant portion of the day' with activities such as getting washed and dressed but this will only entitle you to the lower rate for which you may already qualify via the 'cooking test' route.

It may be helpful to seek advice on how best to fill either the ICB questionnaire or the DLA claim form both of which are rather long. Contact your local Citizen's Advice Bureau, Council Advice Shop or one of the ME charities (see Appendix; 'Useful Addresses').

My local DSS has told me that I don't have enough NI contributions to get Incapacity Benefit. What am I supposed to live on?

You can claim Disability Living Allowance (see above). You can also claim Severe Disablement Allowance (SDA) which is not means-tested and is, therefore, not dependent on how much income or capital you have. You can also claim Income Support (and Housing Benefit and Council Tax Benefit from your Local Authority) depending on your income and capital. SDA is counted in full as income for IS but will qualify you for the Disability Premium on IS. The IS with Disability Premium may exceed what you receive on SDA so you will then be paid the difference as Income Support. To qualify for SDA you must be assessed as eighty per cent disabled (see below). You have to make a written claim and a doctor known as an adjudicating medical practitioner will, after giving you an examination, decide whether or not you are eighty per cent disabled. You are automatically deemed to satisfy the eighty per cent rule if you receive the higher or middle rate of the DLA care component or the higher rate of DLA mobility component.

My wife has had to give up work to look after me and money is now very tight. Are there any benefits she can claim?

If you receive either the higher or middle rates of the care component of DLA your wife can claim Invalid Care Allowance (ICA) as long as she looks after you for 35 hours or more a week. This benefit is not means-tested. Depending on your income and capital your wife can also claim the means-tested Income Support (and by extension claim Housing Benefit and Council Tax Benefit from your Local Authority) and the income from your DLA will not be counted. Your wife is not required to be 'available for work' for the purposes of Income Support while she is caring for you for 35 hours a week and she will receive Class 1 National Insurance contributions. However, her Income Support will be reduced by the amount of any Invalid Care Allowance she receives as this is counted as income.

Although I am very ill my claims for disability benefits have been unsuccessful. What should I do?

It can be a blow to be rejected for benefits that you evidently need. First there is the financial worry and second, the daunting prospect of having to go through the whole review and, possibly, appeal process. The last thing you want to do when you are ill is spend your little energy fighting for your rights. Having to do so can only contribute to a feeling that unlike those who receive their benefit with no bother you are, somehow, not a deserving enough case.

The problem with all the disability benefits is that the criteria for claiming them doesn't adequately take into account the effects of chronic illness. There is an emphasis on loss of limbs and motor functions that fails fully to take into account fluctuating conditions or incapacity caused by repetitive action and fatigue. To succeed in a claim for Severe Disablement Allowance, for example, you have to be assessed as eighty per cent disabled. The loss of a foot and hand is defined as one hundred per cent disablement, the loss of a thumb, thirty per cent. But how easy is it to assess less defined disabilities this way? A person with ME may be so severely affected as to be virtually housebound yet not be deemed eighty per cent disabled while someone who is deaf yet has no other disabilities and is perfectly able to work full-time is assessed as one hundred per cent disabled.

DSS claim forms reveal a rather narrow view of disability and it can be difficult to portray the extent of your limitations if you simply answer the questions provided without giving additional information. Both the Incapacity Benefit and Disability Living Allowance forms allow you to expand on the way your particular illness affects you, but this is obviously more demanding on a claimant than being able to simply tick off ,'yes' or, 'no' in the way those with less complicated disabilities are able to do. The onus is put on to you to explain your illness. It is important, therefore, not to understate your problems. Many people with ME tend to do this because they are used to being told that their condition isn't as bad as they think it is. Also, denying the severity of your illness to yourself can be a way of coping.

If you have been unsuccessful in your claims it may be that you failed to give a clear and complete picture, either on your application or at the medical examination, of how ME disables you. With a disease that fluctuates from hour to hour, never mind day to day, it is advisable to describe what you can do on your very worst days and then qualify your answers by saying that sometimes your condition is not so severe. Or if you are able to do something such as lifting a bag of potatoes (one of the tests of incapacity for ICB) but cannot do so repetitively or without feeling ill afterwards you must say so. Next time you have a medical by the Examining Medical Officer do not take a passive role of only answering the questions you are asked but take an active role in providing detailed information on your own initiative.

The procedures for disputing a decision by the DSS differs according to the benefits in question. In general, though, there are two ways to contest a decision; asking for a review and going to appeal. You must normally ask for either of these within three months of the decision being sent to you. The most common procedure is to go first for a review which is simply a matter of writing a letter for a new adjudicating officer to make a decision on the basis of new information that you include. This is your chance to include details about how ME disables you that you may have left out in your original application. If the review is unsuccessful, the next stage is usually to appear before an appeal tribunal – if you are too ill to attend you can be represented without your presence or sometimes a tribunal can be held in your home. At this stage it is worth seeking advice from your local Citizen's Advice Bureau or Welfare Rights Agency. You will find these easily in the phone book. They will be able to help you prepare your appeal and may be able to represent you at the tribunal. If your appeal fails then you may appeal to a Social Security Commissioner. Again you should seek advice on your best strategy for success.

A friend has told me that my local Social Services may be able to help me. What help do they provide and how do I go about getting it?

If you are chronically ill or disabled your local Social Work Department (address in the phone book under Social Work or under the name of your local Regional Council) has to supply certain services under section 2 of the Chronically Sick and

Disabled Persons Act. The services they must provide are:
* practical help at home eg. help with dressing, cooking, getting out of bed or a home help
* radio, television, books or similar leisure facilities (such as talking books)
* help with transport to local authority or voluntary services
* home adaptations or other facilities which would improve your safety, comfort or convenience, eg. alarms or extra heating
* holidays (which may be organised by the local authority, the person themselves or by a carer)
* meals at home or at a day centre
* telephone and equipment to help you use it

These services are your legal right but it is up to the Social Work department to decide what you need. If you tell them you need some help they are bound by law to look into your case and make an assessment of your needs.

To make an assessment, a Social Worker will normally meet you, and your carer if you have one, to talk things over. This is an opportunity for you to find out what services they can provide (as well as those listed above, they may be able to offer respite care, counselling, occupational therapy etc.) and for you to tell them what your needs are.

A big problem for people with ME is that their Social Worker may have no experience of 'invisible' chronic illness. This may result in their failing to recognise even substantial needs simply because you may not look like the other ill or disabled people s/he usually sees. It is very important, therefore, to make it as clear as possible exactly how restricted you are and what services you think might help you. Avoid the temptation to put on a front for your meeting. If, for example, you spend most of your time in bed, don't feel you should make a special effort to get up. Your Social Worker needs to see you as you really are so act as you normally would and feel free to go into detail about the way your illness affects you.

When the Social Work department has made a decision about your needs they will tell you what they can provide or arrange for you. They may write this out in a 'care plan' which you have a right to see. Even if they decide that you do have certain needs they do not have to provide all the help that you need if they do not have enough money. They do, however have to provide those services listed above which come under the Chronically Sick and Disabled Persons Act.

Unfortunately, if you don't agree with their assessment of your needs you have no right of appeal. This is particularly serious for people with a disease like ME about which there is still a lot of ignorance. If you feel you are not getting the help you need you should start with a complaint to the Social Work Department. Every Department now has a new complaints procedure which includes an independent review. They should tell you what it is and how it works. If you have difficulty filling in forms or putting your complaint into words, they have to help you. It may be a good idea at this stage to get help from one of the ME charities or your local Community Health Council (Local Health Council in Scotland).

It can be difficult to take action to win your rights to community care services when you have very little energy especially as those who apply for such help are likely to be the more severely affected. But if you can face complaining, it will make your local Social Work department more aware of the needs of people with all kinds of illness and disability. And the more complaints your local Community Health Council finds out about, the more likely they are to investigate and report on the matter.

The next stage of complaint is to the Local Government Ombudsman who can often sort things out informally. You can also think about seeing a solicitor (you may be able to get Legal Aid) for advice and possible legal action. As a last resort you can complain to the Secretary of State who can hold an enquiry. He has the power to tell the Social Work Department how to operate community care. (All addresses for Community Health Councils, Ombudsman etc. in Appendix III.)

I really need a holiday but can't afford it. Are there any organisations that can help me financially?

Social Services have a legal duty, as described above, to assess your needs for services that can include funding for a holiday. How much money is available for this and whether or not you will be assessed as a high priority is up to your local office.

The Holiday Care Service and the small charity, Give ME a Break both give grants for holidays (addresses in Appendix) but they have limited funds. If you are severely affected it is worth contacting the latter.

NOTE: Always keep copies of any claim forms or letters sent and seek up-to-date information as Welfare Benefit rules may change.

APPENDICES

Appendix I – Useful Exercises

When you have lots of energy you can get away with breathing poorly and getting tense. But people with ME need to conserve the little energy they have and learning to breathe correctly and to relax can help do this. The following exercises won't make you better but will, hopefully, make you feel more rested and better able to cope.

You may find it helpful if a friend or relative reads the exercises out to you – slowly and with lots of pauses to leave enough time between each move – until you get used to them. You should soon know them off by heart and be able to go through them yourself. Alternatively, you could read the exercises out and record them and then listen to your own voice. There are also several audio tapes on the market which lead you through different exercises. See Appendix II; Useful Addresses, under Audio Tapes, for mail-order details.

1 Breathing correctly

Lie on your back on the floor or bed with your eyes closed.

Place your left hand on your chest and your right hand on your stomach. Breathe as you normally do.

If you are overbreathing, the left hand on your chest will rise when you breathe in. If you are breathing properly the right hand on your stomach will gently rise instead. The aim is to breathe in such a way that the hand on your chest rises as little as possible as the air is taken deep into your body. Breathe in and out through the nose.

When you inhale, imagine that the air is entering your nostrils and is being sucked down towards your stomach.

Breathe in and hold for a couple of seconds and then slowly breathe out as your stomach falls as it expels the air. Remember that your chest should rise as little as possible. Try not to take in too much air. You do not need much oxygen when you are lying on the floor.

Practise breathing in and out for 5-10 minutes or longer if you feel like it. With each exhalation, imagine all your tensions flowing out of your body.

2 Basic Relaxation

Lie on your back on the floor or bed, arms resting down your sides and eyes closed. Make sure that you are warm enough and comfortable.

Do a few breathing exercises and with each exhalation imagine the tension in your body flowing out.

Think of your right foot and imagine it floppy and loose. Let out any tension that you feel in your foot. Think of your right ankle and let it relax. Feel your ankle and foot heavy. Feel the gravity of the ground beneath pulling them towards it.

Moving up your leg, think of your right calf, imagine the muscles loose and soft. Relax your calf muscles. Imagine your knee and thigh soft and relaxed. Feel the whole of your right leg heavy and supported by the floor or bed.

Repeat with your left foot and leg.

Imagine your stomach and let all the tension flow out of it. Make sure you are not tensing your stomach while you are breathing. Imagine your buttocks relaxed and heavy against the ground.

Move up your body and relax the muscles in your chest. Feel the tension flow out of your shoulders. Relax your shoulders again, feeling them drop slightly as the tension is released.

Relax your back. Let the ground beneath you support you. Feel your back heavy as you are lying there.

Feel the muscles in the top of your right arm loose and relaxed. Imagine your right elbow heavy and let this feeling spread down to your wrist. Let all the tension out of your right hand. The fingers and thumb should be slightly curled.

Repeat with your left arm and hand.

Imagine your head heavy against the floor or bed. Relax the neck muscles, you do not need to use them as your head is well supported.

Feel the tension released from your jaw. Unclench your teeth and imagine the beginning of a smile. Relax and loosen your tongue and make sure it is not pressed against the roof of your mouth. Imagine the skin on your face smoothed outwards. Relax your forehead and imagine the skin smoothed upwards toward your scalp.

Imagine your eyes are pools of water. Let them feel cool and the eyelids relaxed.

Now think of your whole body and feel all the seperate parts come together into a relaxed whole. Concentrate on the feeling of relaxation casting your mind every so often over any parts of your body that are becoming tense again. Repeat the process of releasing tension as described above if you find that any muscle group is tightening again.

Continue lying relaxed for as long as feels comfortable. This can be anything from five minutes to half an hour.

Although it is most effective when practised lying down, you can do this exercise sitting up and it can be done wherever you happen to be.

NOTE: If you find it difficult to know when your muscles are relaxed, go through the exercise but clenching each muscle group before you relax it. If, for example, you clench your leg muscles you will find that they are hard and tense. When you let this tension go, they will feel loose and soft. By comparing the difference when tensing and relaxing you will soon be able to tell when your muscles are relaxed.

3. Visualisation.

i) Relaxing the Mind

Follow the relaxation exercise as above with your eyes closed.

When your body is completely relaxed imagine in your mind's eye a yellow circle of light. Concentrate on this circle and try to keep it in your mind. Do not worry if the image slips away. Just conjure it up again. After a couple of minutes let this picture go.

Now think of a number and imagine it growing in height until it is as high as you can hold in your mind. Retain this image for a few seconds and then let it go. Think of another number and then slowly start adding numbers to it, placing them side by side in a long row. Think of as many numbers as you can hold in your mind. Concentrate on this row of numbers. Hold the image for a couple of minutes and let them fade into the distance until they disappear.

Now imagine yourself in a dark room sitting comfortably in front of a large television screen.

The screen is blank apart from the word RELAX in bold letters. Concentrate on this word. Do not worry if other words appear or if thoughts keep entering your head. Acknowledge them and then let them go. Concentrate on the word RELAX on the TV screen in front of you for a minute or so. Then let the word get smaller and smaller until it disappears.

Now see the words I AM COMPLETELY RELAXED appear. This sentence starts at the top of the screen and slowly moves down until it reaches the bottom when it disappears. See it appearing again at the top of the screen and repeat the process. Concentrate on this image for 5 minutes or until you feel your mind empty and relaxed.

ii) Getting to Sleep

Relax your body with a relaxation exercise and with your eyes closed follow the visualisation exercise above to relax your mind.

After seeing the sentence I AM COMPLETELY RELAXED replace it with the words I AM FEELING SLEEPY. See this sentence in your mind repeated over and over again. Then see the words I AM GETTING SLEEPIER AND SLEEPIER and concentrate on this sentence until you start to feel drowsy.

Now count slowly backwards from 10. Imagine the number in your mind's eye. Between each number, slowly breathe in and when you slowly breathe out again imagine the word RELAX.

When you reach 4, slowly breathe in, breathe out and imagine the words I AM FEELING VERY DROWSY. When you reach 3, breathe in and out twice and imagine the words I AM GETTING MORE AND MORE DROWSY. When you reach 2, breathe in and out twice and see the words I AM ALMOST ASLEEP NOW. When you reach 1, breathe in and out three times and imagine the words SOON I WILL BE ASLEEP and continue breathing slowly in and out repeating these words in your mind until you fall asleep.

iii) Dealing with anger

Relax your body and follow the breathing exercise above for a couple of minutes. Keep your eyes closed.

Now, with each inhalation, imagine that you are breathing in a sweet aroma. This can be whatever you like, the smell of roses, the smell of freshly baked bread – any smell that you like and feels nourishing to you. As you breathe in this lovely smell, imagine it accompanied by a healing light so that you feel you are breathing in a warm and beneficial substance.

With each exhalation, imagine that you are breathing out all your anger and nasty, difficult feelings in the form of a thick, dark, foul-smelling smoke. Each time you breathe out you rid yourself of more of your anger. Each time you breathe in you replace the evil-smelling, infected smoke with restorative, pure and soothing air.

iv) Dealing with rejection

Relax your body and do some breathing exercises for a few minutes with your eyes closed.

Imagine a tiny dot of extremely bright, white light approaching you from a distance. As it comes nearer, it grows in size. When it reaches you it has turned into a large cloud of brilliant and warm light.

Imagine this light as being healing and full of goodness. See the cloud envelop your body and as it covers you, feel its warmth seeping into you.

Imagine the cloud shrinking in size until it is the size of a golf ball. It is now hovering over your heart. See its brightness and imagine it slowly enter your heart and infuse it with warmth. Let this feeling spread throughout your body.

Now imagine a kind but unknown figure approaching you. You cannot see their face but you know that they care about you and want to see you feeling better. Imagine this figure putting a huge pair of arms around you and imagine yourself crying on their shoulder. Feel these arms comforting you and protecting you from unkind remarks and people who hurt you.

Appendix II – Useful Books

Living with ME by Dr Charles Shepherd. (Cedar, 1995)

Good description of the history of the disease and its symptoms. Well organised and accessible information on coping physically with ME, balanced view on alternative therapies and a fairly detailed overview of your rights as regards the NHS, Social Security benefits and other services available. A useful practical handbook on the physical side of the illness.

Disability Rights Handbook
Available from Disability Alliance (see below for address)

An excellent guide focusing mainly on your rights to welfare benefits. Also proves information on housing and care in the community. Updated annually.

Rights Guide to Non-Means-Tested Benefits
National Welfare Benefits Handbook

Both produced by Child Poverty Action Group (address below). The Rights Guide deals with all the Disability benefits and other non-means-tested benefits and the Handbook with all the means-tested benefits such as Income Support, Housing Benefit etc. The books that advice centres use to advise their clients. Excellent, clearly written guides.

Charities Digest
Available from The Family Welfare Association (address below)

Comprehensive guide to over 1200 charities nationwide with details of their objective and work. Useful for tracking down helpful agencies. Updated annually.

Meditation by Erica Smith and Nicholas Wilks (Optima, 1988)

Straightforward introduction to meditation, its traditions and practice. Clearly describes a range of techniques, including relaxation, visualisation and beneficial breathing, that can be achieved with or without a teacher.

The complete Yoga Book by James Hewitt (Rider, 1993)

Comprehensive guide to all you want to know about yoga including breathing, posture and meditation from beginners to advanced. Enough basic exercises for people limited by ME.

A Woman in your Own Right by Anne Dickson (Quartet, 1987)

Although written for women this is a very useful book for either sex. A very practical guide on how to be more assertive, dealing with put-downs, confrontation, learning to say 'No' and so on.

Making Love by Michael Castleman (Penguin, 1988)

A general guide for both men and women. It doesn't address chronic illness directly but it does have very useful things to say about the effect of stress on libido and love-making and the importance of sensuality in a relationship.

When Bad Things Happen to Good People by Harold S. Kushner (Pan 1982)

A religious (Christian) book that still has something to say to non-believers particularly on the 'reason' for suffering.

Living Creatively with Chronic Illness by Eugenie G. Wheeler and Joyce Dace-Lombard (Pathfinder Publishing, 1989)

A book on chronic illness in general. Its strength lies in the acknowledgment of long-term illness as a serious condition. It offers practical exercises to come to terms with a restricted life but is aimed at those who are still fairly active. The two ME sufferers in the book, for example, are both able to work and socialise and those in a similar situation will find the book useful. For the severely affected and housebound, the upbeat and rather relentless positive tone may irritate and undermine.l

The Fourth Horseman by Andrew Nikiforuk (Cambridge University Press, 1992)

A short and entertaining history of disease in which ME gets a (brief) mention! Interesting for putting illness and others' attitudes towards it in an historical context.

Appendix III – Useful Addresses

Advice and Information

Child Poverty Action Group (CPAG)
1-5 Bath Street
London EC1V 9PY
Produces both the National Welfare Benefits Handbook and Rights Guide to Non-Means-Tested Benefits

Citizens' Advice Bureaux
Local branches in most areas for information on almost any legal or financial matter including housing, employment, welfare rights, debt counselling etc. Look under CAB in the phone book. Most provide advice over the telephone, support and representation for appeals and some may be able to arrange home-visits.

Disability Alliance
Universal House
88-94 Wentworth Street
London E1 7SA
Tel (0171) 247 8776
Campaigning group that provides information and advice on all disability issues but particularly welfare benefits. Publishes the Disability Rights Handbook.

Disabled Living Foundation
380-384 Harrow Road
London W9 2HU
Tel (0171) 289 6111
Information and advice on practical aids. Produces a wide range of fact sheets on, for example, how to choose a wheelchair, footwear for cold feet, how to enhance your mobility etc. Send for a free publications list.

Disability Helpline Wales
3 Links Court
Links Business Park
St Mellons
Cardiff
Tel (01222) 798 633
Information and advice on all aspects of disability.

Disability, Northern Ireland Council on
2 Annadale Avenue
Belfast BT7 3JR
Tel (0232) 491011
Information on all aspects of disability. Can refer you to other relevant organisations in the region.

Disability and Rehabilitation, Royal Association for
12 City Forum
250 City Road
London EC1V 8AF
Tel (0171) 250 3222
Campaigning body that provides information and advice and a wide range of publications, such as 'Holidays in the British Isles' and 'How to push a Wheelchair', as well as leaflets on most aspects of disability. For the more technically minded, they produce many reports and factsheets on legislation

relevant to the ill such as the Community Care Act, the Chronically Sick and Disabled Persons Act 1970 etc. Send for a free publications list. Also has equipment centres in many regions where you can try out various aids.

Disability Scotland
Princes House
5 Shandwick Place
Edinburgh EH2 4RG
Tel (0131) 229 8632
Information on all aspects of disability.

Health Information Service
Freephone 0800 665 544
A free service providing wide range of information on, for example, waiting times or common illnesses.

Social Security, Department of
(Mail Order leaflets)
PO Box 21
Stanmore
Middlesex HA7 1AY
Advice line on benefits for the disabled is available Freephone 0800 882200 Monday to Friday 9am – 4.30 pm.

Audio Tapes

Life Skills
Bowman House
6 Billetfield
Taunton
TA1 3NN
Tel (01821) 451 771
Mail-order cassettes and books to help you relax, assert yourself, control tension etc.

Listening Library
Room 23
12 Lant Street
London SE1 1QH
Tel (0171) 407 9417
National mail-order library supplying talking books and special players, post-free for an annual fee of £25.

Relaxation for Living
168-170 Oatlands Drive
Weybridge KT13 9ET
Tel (01932) 831 000
Mail-order leaflets and relaxation tapes available. Also information about local courses teaching relaxation techniques.

Carers

Carers National Association
29 Chilworth Mews
London W2 3RG
Tel (0171) 724 7776
Provides information and support to carers. A nationwide network of local support groups.

Carers National Association Scotland
11 Queen's Crescent
Glasgow G4 9AS
Tel (0141) 333 9495

Carers National Association Northern Ireland
113 University Street
Belfast BT7 1HP
Tel (01232) 439 843

Crossroads Care Attendant Schemes
10 Regent Place
Rugby
Warwickshire CV21 2PN
Tel (01788) 573 653
Offers carers a break by sending in trained 'care attendants' to look after ill/disabled people. Deal with all sorts of illnesses including ME. Also provide help for children who care for an ill parent. Contact them for information about regional offices in your area.

Volunteer Bureaux, National Association of
St Peters College
College Road
Saltley
Birmingham B8 3TG
Phone for your local Volunteer Bureau or look in the phone book under Volunteer. Matches you with volunteer who may be able to provide range of help eg. driving, gardening, befriending etc.

Counselling

Counselling, British Association for
37a Sheep Street
Rugby
Warwickshire CV21 3BY
Tel (01788) 578 328/9
Information about counselling. Provides names and addresses of qualified counsellors in your area.

See also **ME Association & Action for ME**

Relate (formerly Marriage Guidance Council)
Herbert Gray College
Little Church Street
Rugby CV21 3AP
Tel (01788) 573 241
Local branches in the phone book
Confidential counselling (including sex therapy) for individuals and couples with relationship problems. You do not have to be married. Counselling offered to both straight and gay couples.

Samaritans
*Look in phone book under
Samaritans for your local branch.
Confidential telephone helpline
providing 24hr support. You don't
have to be suicidal to use this
service – it's there for anyone who
feels the need to share what's on
their mind.*

SPOD (The Association to Aid
the Sexual and Personal relationships of people with a
Disability)
286 Camden Road
London N7 OBJ
Tel (0171) 607 8851
*Provides information and support
to people with a disability and/or
their partner. Produces a range of
leaflets and operates a professional
and confidential counselling
service. You can also write to a
SPOD counsellor for advice.*

Family and Education

**Advisory Centre for Education
(ACE)**
1B Aberdeen Studios
22 Highbury Grove
London N5 2EA
Tel (0171) 354 8318
Free telephone advice 2.00-
5.00pm Mon-Fri (0171) 354 8321
*Independent national education
advice centre for parents. Can
advise on educational needs of sick
children and young people including home tuition etc.. Publishes the
Special Education Handbook, a
step-by-step guide through the
intricacies of assessment and state-
menting including relevant
legislation and the review and
appeal system.*

Family Welfare Association
501-505 Kingsland Road
Dalston
London E8 4AU
Tel (0171) 254 6251
*Professional counselling service for
families in distress. Also publishes
the Charities Digest.*

**Invalid Children's Aid
Nationwide**
Allen Graham House
198 City Road
London EC1V 2PH
Tel (0171) 608 2462
*Advises parents on all aspects –
including problems with education
– of caring for an ill/disabled child.*

Continued overleaf

Open College of the Arts
Houdhill
Worsbrough
Barnsley
South Yorkshire S70 6TU
Tel (01226) 730 495
Affiliated to the Open University providing a variety of art related courses eg. art and design, painting, textiles, garden design, art history, music, writing etc. Courses are available with postal tuturial support and no qualifications are necessary. Courses start at £155 and a number of bursaries are available.

Open University
Adviser on Education of
Students with Disabilities
Walton Hall
Milton Keynes MK7 6AA
Tel (01908) 653 442
Range of distant learning courses with options for attending tutorials. Tutorials also available over the phone. You do have to have a certain level of health for OU courses as you need to be able to do 12-15 hours study a week and there are assignments with deadlines within the course. For the more severely affected, study packs are available to work through independently. You only get feedback on these if you pay for assessments and they don't lead to a qualification. Financial assistance available in a means-tested, cash-limited fund.

Holidays

Give ME A Break Fund
c/o Sue Mainwaring
3 Court Cottages
Court Hill
Swanage
Dorset
Holiday information specifically for people with ME with limited grants.

Holiday Care Service
2 Old Bank Chambers
Station Road
Horley
Surrey RH6 9HW
Tel (01293) 776943
Specialises in finding suitable holiday accommodation for those with special needs eg. mobility, dietary etc.

ME Organisations

Action for ME and Chronic Fatigue
P.O. Box 1302
Wells
BA5 2WE
Tel (01749) 670799
24 hour helpline on (0891) 233976 (Calls charged at 39p per minute cheap rate or 49p per minute at all other times. 30% of the call revenue will go to Action for M.E. for research and support service finding.)
Campaigning charity providing information and support to people with M.E. and Chronic Fatigue, their family and friends. Interested in a wide range of therapies it takes a holistic approach to illness which may not suit everyone. Produces various factsheets including a booklet aimed at young people with M.E. Members receive three copies of the journal 'InterAction' (also available on tape), access to information and counselling heplines (confidential counselling service provided by professional counsellors), local group networks, file of recommended doctors, postal M.E. library and other services.

ME Association
Stanhope House
High Street
Stanford-le-Hope
Essex SS17 0HA
Tel (01375) 642466
Advice Line (01375) 361 013
Listening Ear (01375) 642 466
ME charity providing a similar service as Action for ME but more orthodox in its approach. Publishes a quarterly magazine 'Perspectives' and has a network of local groups around the country. Also has a host of special interest groups including a Bedbound Group, Singles Group, Penfriend Group and Carers Group. Leaflets available on a variety of subjects relating to the disease. Listening Ear service is run by lay volunteers with experience of ME who offer support and advice.

ME Association N.Ireland
28 Bedford St
Belfast BT2 7FE
Tel (01232) 439 831

ME Association Scotland
52 St.Enoch Square
Glasgow G1 4AA
Tel (0141) ~~204 3822~~ 943 1313 *(01375 642 466)*

Westcare
155 White Ladies Road
Clifton
Bristol BS8 2RF
Tel (01272) 239 341
Provides information and advice to people with ME, family, friends and health professionals. Offers a counselling service for people in the Bristol area and those willing to travel.

Patients' Rights

Community Health Councils, Association for England & Wales
30 Drayton Park
London N5 1PB
Tel (0171) 609 8405

and

Scottish Association of Health Councils
5 Leamington Terrace
Edinburgh EH10 4JW
Tel (0131) 229 2344

Community Health Councils represent users of the NHS. Although the structure between England & Wales and Scotland is different, the aims are the same. Each council can send you a useful leaflet entitled 'Patients' Rights' covering what services you can expect from your GP, how to change your doctor, how to make a complaint etc. They provide advice and support on how to make a complaint or with any NHS enquiry. You can find your local Health Council in the phone book, in England and Wales under 'Community' and in Scotland under Health Councils, Health Services or the name of your Council (eg. Lothian, Argyll & Clyde).

General Medical Council
44 Hallam Street
London W1N 6AE
Tel (0171) 580 7642

Health Service Commissioner (Ombudsman)
Church House,
Great Smith Street,
London. SW1 3BW
Tel (0171) 276 3000

Health Service Commissioner – Wales
4th Floor
Pearl Assurance House
Greyfriars Road
Cardiff
Tel (01222) 394 621

Health Service Commissioner – Scotland
11 Melville Crescent
Edinburgh EH3 7LU
Tel (0131) 225 7465

Local Government Ombudsman – England
21 Queen Anne's Gate
London SW1H 9BY

or

Beverley House
17 Shipton Road
York YO3 6FZ

Local Government Ombudsman – Wales
Derwent House
Court Road
Bridge End
Mid Glamorgan CF31 1BN

Local Government Ombudsman – Scotland
23 Walker Street
Edinburgh EH3 7HX
Tel (0131) 225 5300

Members of Parliament
You can write to your MP at:
Palace of Westminster
London SW1 OAA

**Secretary of State for England
& Wales**
Richmond House
79 Whitehall
London SW1A 2NS

Secretary of State for Scotland
Scottish Office
New St Andrew's House
Edinburgh EH1 3TG

Penfriends
*Both the ME charities run free
penfriend services aimed at different groups such as young people,
singles and carers. Contact them
for more details.*

*There are also a number of friend-
ship clubs that charge a small fee.
These include:*

Budding Friends
P.O. Box 106
Ampthill
Bedford MK45 2AT

International Penfriends
(for penfriends from around
the world)
P.O. Box 340
Dublin 12
Ireland

*If your confidence is at a low ebb
there is a self-help group for people
– especially those with disabilities –
who have become, particularly,
emotionally isolated:*

Outsiders Club
P.O. Box 4ZB
London W1A 4ZB
Tel 0171 739 3195

Pets

Dogs for the Disabled
Frances Hay House
Banbury Road
Bishops Tachbrook
Leamington Spa
Warwickshire CV33 9UQ
Tel (01926) 651 179

Support Dogs
PO Box 447
Sheffield
S7 2YY
Tel (01742) 320026
*Both charities train dogs to assist
ill/disabled owners in everyday life
by carrying out various tasks eg.
fetching and carrying, picking up
dropped objects, even emptying the
washing machine.*

Index